GREAT JEWISH PORTRAITS IN METAL

Gift of Mr. and Mrs. Selig Burrows

Great Jewish Portraits in Metal
SELECTED PLAQUES AND MEDALS FROM THE SAMUEL FRIEDENBERG COLLECTION OF THE JEWISH MUSEUM

Edited by Daniel M. Friedenberg

Introduction by Cecil Roth

PUBLISHED BY SCHOCKEN BOOKS FOR The Jewish Museum
UNDER THE AUSPICES OF *The Jewish Theological Seminary of America*

Copyright © 1963 by The Jewish Museum
Library of Congress Catalog Card No. 63-13345
Manufactured in the United States of America

Contents

Samuel Friedenberg.

PLAQUE: *Cast bronze, 9″ x 7⅜″, by Ludwig Wolpert. FB 1067.*

FOREWORD

In assembling his collection of medals and plaques, the late Samuel Friedenberg was governed by two objectives: to gather medals of Jewish interest in the widest sense, including those of non-Jewish origin, with bearing on the Bible and Jewish history; and to commemorate Jewish notables in both the fields of Jewish scholarship and general civilization. Samuel Friedenberg thus created an encyclopedia of Great Jewish Portraits in Metal, of which this book gives a selection of some two hundred personalities.

In the Introduction, the historian Cecil Roth, a collector of renown in his own right, first tells the story of the Jewish medal and then of the Friedenberg Collection itself, the latter having been assembled over a period of almost three decades. Since the number of medals of specific Jewish content are historically few, it was necessary for the late Samuel Friedenberg to commission plaques as well. Several well-known artists were engaged for this purpose.

The distinction between medal and plaque is fundamental to the understanding of the art of creating metal commemoratives. The medal, related to the round coin, presents two sides, called the obverse and reverse. The plaque, whose outline is frequently not round, has its representation on one side alone. While the medal is usually struck, the plaque is always cast. Because of this freer technique, the creator of a plaque does not need the experience of a medalist. This difference also influences size. Medals may not exceed an average size of about two inches in diameter, while plaques are not so restricted. Some of the plaques in the Friedenberg Collection measure fifteen by ten inches, though the majority, deliberately kept within certain proportions, do not exceed six to seven inches in their larger dimension.

The artists employed by Samuel Friedenberg were given great liberty in the matters of size and shape when casting the plaques. It is quite apparent, when viewing the Collection, that the size had nothing to do with the importance of the personality depicted. The individual approaches of the various artists are also evident in other matters. Ivan Sors, who did the majority of the plaques, was trained as a graphic artist. He thus attempted to indicate on the background of the plaques the field in which the person portrayed attained his or her prominence, adding a picturesque effect to the plaques thus treated. Other artists, reared in the tradition of the purely sculpturesque, like Benno Elkan and F. J. Kormis, approached the more classical rendering of the human likeness. Due to the neutral background, these plaques come closer to medals.

The medals in the Friedenberg Collection follow the method employed since antiquity, with the emphasis on the sculptural feeling for the human head. These medals thus are direct ancestors of the minting procedures used for coins. One can say that wherever the artist followed the basic concepts of classic art, the medals are aesthetically of the finest quality. There are several examples of this kind in the Collection, especially those of the last century, which technically and artistically reveal this classic approach.

While for almost all the medals the profile view of the person is preferred, a number of plaques show the portrait either *en face* or in three-quarter profile—both very difficult to execute in relief technique. They were not so depicted by the artist because of a desire to complicate the work but rather by the limitation of the available material from which he had to draw his portrayal: pictures or photographs. Most of the plaques are based on this kind of source material. It was left to the imagination and intuition of the artist to rise above this limitation and portray the subject from very limited knowledge.

Above and beyond these considerations, it must be kept in mind that this book does not stress the artistic aspect. Its intent is to bring to life Jewish history through the commemoration of outstanding personalities.

Credit should be given to Dr. Guido Schoenberger, Rabbi Moshe Davidowitz, and Dr. Jacob Leff, who volunteered their time for the creation of this book, as well as Mr. William Fleig, Mr. Tom Freudenheim, Mrs. Sybil Langer, and Mrs. Janet Solinger, whose personal interest in the project went far beyond their professional duties.

University of Judaism   STEPHEN S. KAYSER
Los Angeles

Introduction

GREAT JEWISH PORTRAITS IN METAL

BY CECIL ROTH

I

RECENT RESEARCH on the fascinating topic of the relationship of the Jews towards representational art has made it clear that the ideas which prevailed until a short while ago were by no means correct. Notwithstanding the stern prohibition against the delineation of the human or animal form which would superficially seem to be embodied in the Ten Commandments and elsewhere in the Bible, there were long periods in history, as we now know, when the Jews had no inhibitions of this nature, and made lavish use of artistic embellishments—comprising also representations of the human form and scenes out of the Bible—in their homes, their synagogues, and their libraries. Yet in spite of this, it is generally held that even at periods of the greatest liberalism some reticence persisted with regard to three-dimensional representations, for here what was in question was definitely a "graven image," such as is most specifically forbidden by the Bible. Hence it appeared to be axiomatic that in antiquity the Jews could have known nothing in the nature of medals. This is borne out by the fact that the Jewish coins of the classical period, though sometimes executed with a high degree of technical efficiency, bore only decorative symbols and not portraits or human representations such as figure on contemporary Greek or Roman coins; and although in outlying areas subject to their sway one or two rulers of the Herodian house were at times more venturesome, even the Roman procurators did not include any such details on their coins in Judaea. Indeed, the Jews of the Second Temple period stoutly fought at moments of heightened patriotism against the introduction into Palestine even of animal figures molded in the round, though it may be suspected, however, that these objections were sometimes actuated as much by anti-Roman prejudice under a religious mask as by authentic religious orthodoxy.

Yet in spite of all this, the Rabbis of the Talmud, familiar as they were with coins and medals in the world in which they lived, could envisage the existence of similar objects in a Jewish context. One passage, for example, fancifully spoke of portrait coins which bore the likenesses of Abraham and Sarah, of David and Solomon (Babylonian Talmud: Baba Kama, 97b), though, to be sure, the medieval commentators tried to explain this away by suggesting that not the likenesses but the names were engraved. While the eminent thirteenth-century authority, Rabbi Meir of Rothenburg, objected to illuminated prayerbooks mainly because they might distract the attention of the worshipper, he considered three-dimensional representations

Benjamin ben Eliahu Be'er.
Medal: Cast bronze, diam. 6⅞". FB 906.

[11]

Elia de Latas.
Medal: Cast bronze, diam. 1½″. FBG 66.

Eleazer ben Samuel of Brody.
Medal: Copper, diam. 1⅞″. FB 160.

of animals to be objectionable in their own right. Yet some Jewish contemporaries of his, at least in England and in Spain, had signet rings which embodied not merely representations of animals, but also human heads. Such persons would presumably have had no serious objections to owning portrait-medals, but at that time and in that environment the question simply did not arise.*

Conditions changed in this respect at the period of the Renaissance, especially in Italy. Now the classical conception of the commemorative portrait-medal was renewed; now first-class craftsmen imbued with the classical spirit devoted their genius to this branch of art; and now there came into existence, for the first time since classical Alexandria, Jewish communities which, without surrendering their Jewishness, were wholly absorbed in their environment and expressed their Jewish lives in terms of the artistic standards and interests of that environment. If Italian gentiles of the upper class had their medals, Italian Jews of the upper class, so near to them in culture and outlook, wanted them as well.

The oldest extant is *sui generis*, and still presents something of a mystery. The first specimen to come to light was found in the seventeenth century in the bed of the river Rhone at Fourvières. The obverse embodies a laurel-crowned head in the classical style facing right, surrounded by a long and enigmatic Hebrew inscription with the word *umilitas* below in Latin and the equivalent in Greek. When it was first discovered it was ascribed to the ninth century and naïvely believed to commemorate the Emperor Louis the Debonnaire. Long afterwards, however, it was noticed that the Hebrew inscription embodies an acrostic which gives the name "Benjamin son of Rabbi Eliahu Be'er the physician." The date is indicated in a curious Latin inscription on the reverse (*Post tenebra spero lucem felicitatis index dies ultimus D.III.M.*), though it is not quite clear whether this is intended to imply 1497 or 1503. In either case, the subject cannot very well be the famous Italian Jewish physician Elijah ben Sabbatai Be'er, who was in attendance on the Pope and many ruling houses in his day, and was, as "Elias Sabot," summoned to England in 1410 to attend the ailing King Henry IV. Presumably it was his grandson and namesake who flourished long after, unless by some chance this was a posthumous commemoration. However that may be, it is highly doubtful whether the classical head—very similar to the conventional portraits of the Emperor Constantine the Great—is intended to represent the likeness of the person mentioned. This trilingual medal, notwithstanding all that has been written about it, hence remains enigmatic, with no companion or parallel, Jewish or non-Jewish. Nothing could be more ludicrous than the statement in one of the standard works of reference that it was struck by

---

* It may be observed at this point that the military medal to signalize service in the field (the sense in which the term is now most frequently used) is first recorded, as is believed, in a Jewish context. When in the second century B.C.E. the Hasmonean High Priest Jonathan led his Jewish contingents to aid the Syrian King Alexander, he received on each occasion among other rewards (according to Josephus) "a golden button, which it is the custom to give to Royal Kinsmen." These honorary awards of golden plaques are, according to the *Encyclopaedia Britannica*, "the earliest form of medal to commemorate war service."

the Jews of Rome in 1504 to honor Pope Julius II! Incidentally, the lavish use of Hebrew on it renders possible, if not probable, the hypothesis that the anonymous artist was in fact a Jew.

In the course of the sixteenth century, in the Renaissance noonday, a small number of conventional Jewish portrait-medals began to make their appearance. We know of only three, but they are so prodigiously rare (of one indeed only one specimen is recorded, and that no longer extant!) that it is by no means unlikely that others, yet unrecorded, may in fact have been struck. They are competently executed by fashionable medalists of the day in the style in which they did their other work. Their Jewish interest is restricted to the subject and is in no way indicated by the treatment. (We know of one Jewish medalist of the time, Moses da Castellazzo of Venice, Mantua, and Ferrara, but his coreligionists did not, apparently, entrust him with any commissions, and indeed no specimen of his work has been traced.) It is to be noted that these are not commemorative medals. They were not struck in honor of the persons whose effigies they bear, but were commissioned by them or their relatives like painted portraits, in the same way as their wealthy gentile contemporaries gave such commissions to fashionable artists. A point of some interest emerges in connection with this. We have seen above that, whatever the inhibitions among Jews against representational art, a three-dimensional representation was by universal agreement considered more objectionable than a two-dimensional one. Yet we know of drawings and paintings of contemporary Jews, commissioned by them or executed for their own purposes, only from the beginning of the seventeenth century—the three-dimensional medals thus anticipating the two-dimensional portraits by fully half a century.

One of the medals in question is indirectly connected, as is that of Benjamin ben Eliahu Be'er, with a well-known Papal physician. It bears on one side the elegantly bearded likeness of Elijah (Elia) de Latas or Lattes, designated as *ebreo* (the Jew), and on the reverse that of his mother, Rica. Of the subject we know little, except that Elijah's father was Immanuel Lattes, a highly esteemed physician and astronomer active at the Papal court, who in turn was the son of the yet more famous physician-astronomer, Bonet de Lattes. There seems indeed to have been no reason for the commemoration of Rica and Elijah Lattes except that they could afford it, but this is a very fine specimen of the medalist's craft of the Renaissance period.

The same may be said of the medal of the Ferrara Jewish communal leader, Abraham Emmanuel Norsa (c. 1505–1579), made in 1557. The artist responsible for this was the distinguished and versatile Sienese artist Pastorino de Pastorini, mint-master at Ferrara from 1554 to 1559, one of the most competent Italian medalists of the day. It is typical of his graceful, facile, and somewhat superficial treatment, showing the wealthy banker in much the same costume and with much the same bearing as the gentile patricians so often depicted in this medium. In appearance, indeed, the portrait is very similar to that executed in 1556 by the same artist of the exiled English nobleman, Edward Courteney, Earl of Devonshire.

In this same year he executed the best known and loveliest of the Jewish

Hasmonean, Second Century B.C.E.
Coin: Silver, diam. 11/16″.
Friedenberg-Stein Collection.

Bar Kochba Revolt, 135 C.E.
Coin: Silver, diam. 1″.
Friedenberg-Stein Collection.

Local German, 11th-12th century. Initials or names in Hebrew.

Coin: Silver, diam. ⅝". FB 340.

Abraham Abrahamson (1754-1811).

Plaque: Cast bronze, diam. 4¼", by I. Sors. FB 550.

Daniel Itzig, 1793.

Medal: Silver, diam. 2¹⁄₁₆", by A. Abrahamson. FB 73.

medals of the Renaissance period, though the initial *P* with which it is signed has been interpreted in this case by some experts as referring to another eminent artist in this medium, Giovanni Paoli Poggini. The medal in question has its interest enhanced because the subject is feminine.* Also uniface, it represents a young woman, facing left, dressed in the height of Renaissance fashion, like any young Italian noblewoman of the period. A stiff embroidered collar supports the back of her neck, and the veil from her pearl-embroidered headdress descends over her shoulders. The name is given *in Hebrew letters* as Gracia Nasi, with the addition in Latin that the damsel was age eighteen. It was once imagined that this represented the famous, redoubtable, heroic Dona Gracia Nasi (c. 1510–1569), alias Beatrice de Luna (widow of the Lisbon banker, Francisco Mendes) who, born as a Marrano in Portugal, became, on her husband's death, one of the most active businesswomen in Europe, hobnobbed with royalty, organized a sort of underground railway to assist her fellow Marranos to escape from Portugal to lands of freedom, spent some years living in high style in Ferrara where she became known as a patron of letters, and thence in 1552–1555 made her way to Constantinople where until her death she wielded a powerful, if indirect, influence on public affairs. But in 1556 she was no longer living in Ferrara, and was a mature lady in the mid-forties, not a nubile damsel of eighteen. Unless, therefore, this is a representation executed by Pastorino from a portrait of thirty years before (and the costume would argue against this, apart from inherent improbability), this must represent a lesser person: the great Dona Gracia Mendes' niece and namesake who, like the older woman, spent some time in Ferrara in the course of her odyssey from Western Europe to Constantinople, and remained there for a time after the head of the family left for Turkey. It was probably at Ferrara that she first adopted Judaism openly, and the inscribing of her name here in Hebrew characters, obviously at her request, is the sign of her intense pride in the ancestral faith to which she had so adventurously returned (as well, incidentally, as of the gentile artist's willingness to collaborate in signalizing that consummation). She had married Don Samuel Nasi, brother of the famous Don Joseph Nasi, Duke of Naxos, and possibly this medal was struck to celebrate the happy event. Later, she too was to play a resplendent part in the life of the Jews in Constantinople.

It is curious that, after this little group of Renaissance Jewish portrait medallions of the mid-sixteenth century, nothing more of this sort was to emerge for another two hundred years.† In part this was in consequence of the influence of the Counter Reformation, which thrust the Italian Jews into ghettos and cut off the cordial relations that had previously prevailed between them and their neighbors, including the artists who collaborated with them. Even so, it is strange that precisely in this period the por-

---

* See biography section, p. 84.

† The portrait-medal by Jacques Jonghelink of the ex-Marrano Calvinist leader, Luis Perez of Antwerp, struck for his sixty-sixth birthday in 1597, need hardly be taken into account in this connection, nor that (no longer traceable) of his kinswoman Ursula Lopez, widow of Martin Perez and aunt of Michel de Montaigne (c. 1580).

traiture of Jews, often by Jewish artists, became fashionable, such portraits being engraved in some countries for wider circulation. In fact, the next Jewish portrait-medallion in date known to us is a poorly executed specimen made in 1735 to commemorate the appointment of Rabbi Eleazer ben Samuel of Brody as Chief Rabbi of the Ashkenazi community of Amsterdam, on the one side bearing an undistinguished likeness of the scholar in question reading a book, and on the other a lengthy Hebrew inscription. Executed in silver as well as in bronze, this is the earliest Jewish medal known to us certainly to have been made by a Jewish craftsman, the person responsible (who gives his initials on the obverse) being a certain Joel, son of Rabbi Lippman Levi, whom we know as a medalist only by this production. However, his daring experiment did not meet with wholehearted approval, and the cantankerous Rabbi Jacob Emden, when he was consulted, stated roundly (Responsa, clxx) that it was an unquestionable contravention of Jewish law—indeed, his own father, the famous Haham Zevi, had refused to sit even for an ordinary portrait when he visited London, though this was by now considered an excess of piety.

Within a generation of this time conditions changed, for a number of fairly gifted professional Jewish medalists began to emerge, some of whom, incidentally, devoted their attention to Jewish subjects. This was not in every respect a new phenomenon, however. In the technical operation of the minting of coins, in essentials not very different from that of the casting of medals, Jews had already been intimately involved for a very long while. It is true that no coins were issued by the Jewish sovereigns in Bible times—they were not indeed known anywhere as yet. The first minted by a Jewish authority, for the use of the Jewish community and presumably at the hands of Jewish craftsmen, date back in fact to the Hasmonean period, toward the end of the second century before the Christian era. The series continued, with occasional gaps, until the period of the Bar Kochba revolt, about two and a half centuries later; and though, as mentioned above, no portraits or human likenesses were involved, a relatively high standard of technical efficiency and artistic merit was sometimes attained. Thereafter for eighteen hundred years no Jewish state could issue currency (although a Jew named Julius Popper minted some gold coins at El Paramo in South America in 1889 to meet a local shortage). On the other hand, in the medieval world Jews not infrequently figured as mint-masters, were responsible for the issue of coinage, and, in some cases at least, must have been intimately responsible for their design and execution. It is said, for example, that the earliest Arab coinage was minted in Baghdad in the seventh century by the Jew, Sumeir. A century before this there was a Jewish minter named Priscus in France, who was assisted in his work by one Domnulus, who, judging by his name, may also have been a Jew. In central Europe later on the mints were not infrequently managed by Jews, and some local German coinage of the eleventh and twelfth centuries bears their initials or names in Hebrew. But the most remarkable instances come from Poland, where a whole series of twelfth- and thirteenth-century bractates (i.e., uniface coins) have fairly lengthy Hebrew inscriptions giving the sovereign's name or other details. It can

Marcus Herz, ca. 1800.

Medal: Silver, diam. 1⅝", by A. Abrahamson. FB 25X.

Solomon Hirschel, Chief Rabbi of England, 1816.

Medal: Cast aluminum, diam. 2⅜". FB 444.

Fire in the Frankfurt Judengasse, 1711.

Medal: Silver, diam. 1¹¹⁄₁₆". FB 281.

[15]

Intervention of Maria Theresa, Edict of Expulsion from Prague, 1748.

Medal: Cast silver, diam. 2½″. FB 267.

Joseph II—Edict of Toleration, 1781.

Medal: Silver, diam. 1⅝″. FB 223.

Napoleonic Sanhedrin, 1806.

Medal: Bronze, diam. 1⅝″. FB 145.

hardly be doubted that in these cases, at least, the actual craftsmen were Jews, who thus must have had an inkling of the medalist's art.*

An impetus came to this latent tendency at the beginning of the false dawn of enlightenment. Jewish painters were still relatively few, for that calling was partly dependent even now on various factors, social and professional, which presented occasional difficulty for the Jew. On the other hand, the traditional Jewish professions of itinerant pewter-engraver or seal-cutter, so common especially in central Europe, led smoothly and naturally to medal-engraving. Thus in the second half of the eighteenth century a number of Jews began to attain competence and even prominence in this calling. Samuel Yudin (1730–1800) cut coins and medals for the Court of St. Petersburg, including a medal to commemorate the victory at Poltava over Charles XII; Aaron Jacobsohn was appointed court engraver in Copenhagen in 1750; Abraham Aaron (1744–1842) worked at the Courts of Mecklenburg and Stockholm, and cut many medals in the classical style which were highly regarded in their day. The best known and most competent of all were the Berlin court medalists, Jacob Abraham (1723–1800) and his son, Abraham Abrahamson (1754–1811). The latter produced a series of distinguished, if somewhat mechanical, portrait-medals in the classical style in honor of the leaders of German intellectual life. Among them he included his coreligionist Moses Mendelssohn, a fine and characteristic production, in honor of the publication in 1775 of Mendelssohn's famous book *Phaedon.*† Among his other productions were a number of other portrait-medals of persons of the Mendelssohnian circle: Daniel Itzig, in honor of his seventieth birthday (1793); Lippman Mayer, in honor of his seventy-third birthday (1803); Marcus Herz (c. 1800); and others. A few similar works were produced elsewhere by other Jewish medalists, whose tradition continued into the nineteenth century. Thus among the many fine medals by Charles Wiener, a member of an outstanding family of craftsmen—associated also with the earliest Belgian postage-stamps—is one of Aristide Astruc, appointed Grand Rabbi of Belgium in 1866. Besides Leopold and Charles Wiener, nineteenth-century Jewish medalists of this generation included also E. A. Soldi in Paris and A. G. Grichliches in Russia; while somewhat later Artur Lowenthal, who executed a particularly brilliant medal of his old friend Albert Einstein in 1948, was perhaps the outstanding medalist of his time in the classical tradition.

As Jews were accepted into western society, gentile artists assumed commissions to portray notable Jews, as in the days of the Renaissance. Examples are the pleasing medal of Gershom Mendez Seixas, the patriot

---

* It is said also, but without proof, that some portrait-medals produced in Prague about 1600 were the work of local Jewish goldsmiths.

† It is said that the bust of Moses Mendelssohn, thus portrayed in full three dimensions by Peter Anton Tessart (1785) is the earliest known representation of a Jew in this manner. But this is incorrect; a hundred years before this, the Dutch sculptor Rombout Verhulst executed a bust of the Sephardi communal magnate, Antonio Lopes Suasso, Baron d'Avernas le Gras (1614–1685)—a characteristic production of the period including even the full-bottomed periwig.

minister of the American Revolution—the earliest such production in America of Jewish interest—and the commercial production in honor of Solomon Hirschel, Chief Rabbi of England, produced on the occasion of their deaths in 1816 and 1842, respectively. Many pages would be needed to give a mere list of the portrait-medals of Jews produced in the nineteenth and twentieth centuries, only a minority being represented in the context of their activities in the Jewish community. Indeed their association with the community was often extremely tenuous.

Meanwhile, in addition to the portrait-medal, another type of medal began to become popular: the commemorative medal (sometimes also bearing a portrait), struck to signalize some important event of recent history. The earliest of such medals of Jewish interest recorded is one said to commemorate the participation of the Jews in the defense of Buda against the Turks in 1686; at the same time, the Jews were in fact accused of playing the reverse role, though it is conceivable that a medal of this sort was struck and circulated in order to rebut the charge. When a disastrous fire, caused, it was alleged, by the unfortunate experiments of a venerated Cabbalist Rabbi, burned down a good part of the Frankfurt Judengasse in 1711, a medal depicting the scene was struck. And in 1748 another commemorated the repeal, at the intervention of the British, Dutch, and Danish governments, of Maria Theresa's cruel edict expelling the Jews from Prague.

Towards the end of the century the atmosphere changed, and medals were issued celebrating smoother events in Jewish experience: the Emperor Joseph II's Edict of Toleration in 1781; the kindly relations between his Jewish subjects and the Landgrave of Hesse and his consort in 1790; the emancipation of the Jews in the Batavian Republic in 1796; the amelioration of the state of Russian Jews in the false dawn initiated by Czar Alexander I in 1805; the assembly of the Napoleonic Sanhedrin in 1806; the emancipation of the Jews of Westphalia by Jerome Bonaparte (by A. Abrahamson) in 1808; and so on. Occasionally the Jews commemorated significant events of internal history, without ostentatious demonstrations of loyalty such as were customary in these cases. Outstanding from this point of view was the medal struck in 1840 recording the mission of Sir Moses Montefiore and Adolphe Crémieux to Damascus to secure the release of the unfortunate Jews accused of a ritual murder—the first triumph of Jewish diplomacy of this type. It may be noted that these commemorative issues culminated in the famous medal by Samuel Friedrich Beer in honor of the Second Zionist Congress in 1898.

In due course, Jews had also begun to issue medals to signalize not great public events but the petty chronicle of their communities: for example, the founding of the communal school, the Wilhelmschule, at Berlin in 1791; the inauguration of the Adath Jeshurun, the earliest "progressive" Jewish congregation in the world, in Amsterdam in 1800; the building of the new synagogue at Bordeaux in 1810; the laying of the cornerstone (1824) and dedication (1826) of the new synagogue at Munich.

Private commemorative medals also made their appearance from time to time. In Holland, it was not unusual to strike an engraved token to

Emancipation of Jews of Westphalia by Jerome Bonaparte, 1808.

Medal: Silver, diam. 1¹¹⁄₁₆", by A. Abrahamson. FB 221.

Montefiore & Crémieux—Damascus Affair, 1840.

Medal: Silver, gilded, diam. 1¹¹⁄₁₆". FB 90.

Second Zionist Congress, 1898.

Medal: Bronze, diam. 2½", by Samuel Beer. FB 155.

New Synagogue of Munich, 1826.
Medal: Silver, diam. 1½",
by A. L. Loewenbach. FB 214.

Judaea Capta—Vespasian.
Medal: Bronze, diam. 1⁵⁄₁₆". FB 1057

Israel Liberata.
Medal: Gold, diam. 1¹⁄₁₆". FB 1095.

mark a significant wedding anniversary, such as a silver wedding. The earliest known is of 1714, bearing, however, only a plain inscription. Similarly, medals sometimes celebrated a circumcision. One extant, of silver gilt of the middle of the seventeenth century, has on either face a fine representation of a scene from the life of David, and probably commemorates the entry into the covenant of a child of that name.

In addition to the "Jewish" medals mentioned above, there is another category of what might be termed anti-Jewish medals: associated with Jews, that is, but in an adverse sense.* A typical example is that commemorating the baptism of a Jew named Michael in Prague in 1659, showing on one side the ceremony, on the other, the baptism of Jesus in the Jordan. Again, in 1670 a medal was struck to commemorate the three hundredth anniversary of the Desecration of the Host in Brussels, a preposterous charge which had led in 1370 to the barbarous judicial murder of a number of Jews. Another, on the four hundred and fiftieth anniversary, was issued in 1820. In a similar category is the medal, bearing on one side a portrait and on the other the gallows scene, struck in gloating exaltation in 1738 at the time of the execution of Joseph Süss Oppenheimer, the ill-fated Jewish minister at the court of Württemberg, the notorious "Jew Süss." Germany was, of course, the classic land of such productions. Here from the close of the seventeenth century there were issued various *Kornjude* medals, as they are termed, showing on the obverse a Jew with a sack of corn on his back and on the reverse a ring with a lengthy inscription, blaming the Jews for cornering wheat and thus forcing up the price of bread.

There is one other category of medal without any direct Jewish connection but, for one reason or another, of Jewish interest. For example, the very fine English medal struck to celebrate the defeat of the Grand Armada in 1588 bears at the summit the name of God in Hebrew characters, as do also some contemporary Scottish and Danish coins. More conspicuous are the fine English medals (presumably by continental craftsmen) with the portraits of the respective rulers, struck in celebration of the assumption of the role of Head of the Church by King Henry VIII in 1545, and to commemorate the accession of his son Edward VI in 1547. Both of these bear long inscriptions in Hebrew, as well as in Latin and Greek, thus completing the number of the three recognized classical languages of the Renaissance. These medals with all their imperfections are, incidentally, an interesting testimony to the birth of Hebrew scholarship among English scholars.

In the Renaissance, a number of spurious medals purporting to be of

---

* The prototype for these perhaps was the Roman "Judaea Capta" coin issued by Vespasian and other emperors of his house to commemorate the destruction of Jerusalem in the year 70: this had its rejoinder in the similar "Israel Liberata" medal issued in Jerusalem in 1958, showing under the Palmtree of Judah, instead of a weeping mother or the personification of the conquered province, a resurgent Jewish family. Another classical medal of immediate Jewish interest is the "Fisca Judaici calumnia sublata," issued by the Roman Emperor Nerva (96–98) to commemorate the alleviation in the conditions for exacting the tax levied on the Jews.

classical origin were struck and put hopefully into circulation, bearing, for example, the hypothetical likenesses of Dido and Priam. Not unnaturally, some enterprising fabricators also called the heroes of the Bible into service for the purpose, going back even as far as Adam and Eve. Azariah de Rossi, the great Jewish savant of the sixteenth century, naïvely records that he saw one purporting to have been struck by King Solomon. Some medals of this type were more closely associated with the Jews by bearing inscriptions in Hebrew. Thus there were quite a number (which continued to be issued down to modern times) showing the horned head of Moses, with an apposite inscription on the reverse. Others, ostensibly ancient, bore the head of Jesus with the name in Hebrew. This in turn links up with a series of spurious shekels or rather shekel-medals, often in brass, bearing inscriptions in modern Hebrew characters (itself a palpable token of spuriousness) which began to make their appearance in the sixteenth century and were obscurely connected in the popular mind with Judas' thirty pieces of silver. Later, somewhat similar counterfeits began to be made by Jews also as pious souvenirs of the ancient shekel of Temple times. All this, however, has only a marginal interest in connection with our present inquiry.

Mention may be made passingly of another subsidiary field of incidental Jewish interest. The popular amulets that were commonly worn at one time by the superstitious bore Cabbalistical signs and sometimes Hebrew letters, reflecting the credence in, and importance attached to, the Jewish mystical lore. Sometimes, the Jews also wore similar objects, but the presence of Hebrew gibberish or characters on them is no proof of Jewish origin. These, the earliest of which were probably made in Italy during the Renaissance, though they remained common throughout western Europe (in particular in Germany) long after, often bear magic squares or the names of angels in Hebrew, together with the effigies of heathen deities and the like (such as Mercury or Jupiter). Even in the case of those of Jewish origin, the Judaic interest is very slight, and they hardly enter even marginally into the category of medals.

Other miscellaneous medals of a more or less remote Jewish interest, struck in different countries and under widely different auspices, may be mentioned at random. Dutch Jewish shipowners such as Joseph de la Penha (the same to whom King William III is said to have conceded the territory of Labrador) would present medals to ship captains in their service for meritorious action at sea, for example, in this case, beating off two enemy men-of-war. When in 1696 the house of David de Pinto of Amsterdam was attacked by a riotous mob, he presented silver six-styver pieces, suitably engraved, to the members of the militia who arrived in time to save it from destruction. At an exhibition in the Bodleian Library at Oxford in 1944 there were shown two unique eighteenth-century medals struck in 1768 in England to commemorate the capture of the murderer of a Jewish peddler named Wolf Myers. To signalize their gratitude for a poem on Esther, the Parnassim of the Portuguese Jewish community of Amsterdam in 1786 presented a gold medal suitably inscribed to two Dutch

Joseph Süss (Jew Süss) Oppenheimer, 1738; obverse—Portrait; reverse—Gallows scene.

Medal: Pewter, diam. 1½". FB 66.

Kornjude Medals (1694, 1772); obverse—Jew with sack of corn; reverse—rhyme blaming Jews for forcing up price of bread.

Pewter, diam. 1½". FB 233, FB 1013.

Accession of Edward VI, 1547.

Medal: Silver, diam. 2⁷⁄₁₆″. FB 283.

Jesus—name in Hebrew.

Medal: Silver, diam. 1¼″. FB 288.

Judas Shekel (30 pieces of silver), 16th cent.

Coin: Silver, diam. 1⅜″. FB 35.

poetesses famous in their day, Petronella Moens and Adriana van Overstaraten. When the Jewish printer, Joseph Athias, published his famous edition of the Hebrew Bible, notable for the beauty of the type and the accuracy of the text, so much attention was aroused among the learned that the States General of the Netherlands awarded him in 1667 a gold chain and medal (unfortunately not preserved) to signalize their appreciation. There are some English medals issued in the reign of George III by a convivial English club known as the Cabbage Society which bear the word *Purim*, with the year (1780, 1796, 1814), but the implications are obscure; indeed, it is not known for certain that the Society even had any Jewish members.

Of some other medals, and medallions also, one knows unfortunately only from literary sources. According to the 1788 regulations of the educational institution which preceded the Jews' Free School in London, the unfortunate urchins had to wear as part of their school uniform a brass plaque bearing the words in Hebrew: "Holy Confraternity of Talmud Torah: established A.M. 5492." No doubt similar objects were made in other countries.

In England in the reign of George III very little copper coinage was issued and, at the close of the eighteenth century, trading firms and corporations struck tokens for small amounts to meet the deficiency in small change. In due course, these became more elaborate and bore portraits or symbolic figures, sometimes with contemporary allusions. These attracted the attention of collectors, and some persons—such as the London print- and coin-dealer Spence—now began to produce them for their own sake, without regard to practical utility, presumably for publicity. A number of these are of Jewish interest and come virtually under the category of medals. For example, in the closing years of the eighteenth century, Spence produced a number of such tokens bearing the bust of Lord George Gordon, with the slouched hat and long beard which he adopted after his conversion to Judaism, and various patriotic and antirevolutionary slogans or symbols (not with any apparent antisemitic intention, but rather intended as a reminder of, and warning against, the horrors of the Gordon Riots of 1780). A few other tokens of around 1790 showed the bust of Daniel Mendoza, the boxer, sometimes with a prizefight on the reverse.[*] One of 1791, of exceptional rarity, bears together with his bust that of another prizefighter, William Ward, and on the reverse a representation of the fight between them. In due course, such tokens became fashionable, and private persons issued them for the fun of the thing. The example was apparently set, as a matter of fact, by a Jewish numismatist, collector, and patron of the arts, David Alves Rebello of Hackney, then a country village not far from London. From 1795 he began to issue his "Hackney Promissory Tokens," ten in silver and some two dozen in copper, promising to pay one penny on demand. They usually bear a representation of Hackney Church and a coat of arms, but one has the phrase *memoria in aeterna*

---

[*] See biography section, p. 130.

[20]

and Rebello's name, apparently having been issued by his son in his father's memory.

Another quite different subsidiary field of Jewish medal-collecting is constituted by the Jewish community tokens and jetons* in which the Friedenberg collection is particularly strong. The most common of these were sometimes used in many communities as a substitute for currency, in order to make improper use impossible, sometimes because the amounts in question were too small to have an equivalent in coined money. They are in a way the counterpart in late Jewish life to the *tesserae* issued to the populace in ancient Rome to be exchanged for grain, or as admission tokens to the circuses. Thus, for example, in all manner of communities, from the Balkans to Poland, such tokens were minted (or occasionally printed, an equivalent to paper money) by the community to distribute to paupers in charity. They could then be exchanged, perhaps only in recognized stores, for the necessities of life. In Russia, tokens of a fraction of a kopek were minted by the communities, with the consent of the government, for distribution as alms by the poorest section of the community, who could not forgo the luxury of charity but for whom even a single kopek constituted an appreciable sum; the beggar who received a sufficient number of these was then able to exchange them for current coin of the realm which would be accepted in the shops. Such trivial tokens are thus monuments to the insatiable passion for performing works of charity, even by the poorest class, which was one of the characteristics of Jewish life in the past. Again, in some communities (e.g., in Italy) the inconsiderable fee for the ritual slaughter of chickens, brought by the householder to the communal *shochet*, was paid by means of similar tokens, a number of which presumably could be purchased at one time for periodical use as required. In Poland, such tokens were termed *koropka* (i.e., box), which was also the name for the community tax on *shechita*, the shochet having by his side a box in which the fee was deposited.

Another common category of such jetons was issued as it were for purposes of identification, as passes or certificates of membership. Jetons were known, for example, in Amsterdam as early as the closing years of the seventeenth century (1671 is the first recorded) for mourners accompanying funerals. Sometimes, on the other hand, in the German-speaking lands, a jeton bore the name of the person to whom it was issued and thus certified to his affiliation with some particular communal institution, a usage not uncommon also in the general world, like a membership card today. A *mohel* would sometimes issue a similar object to a child whom he circumcised; and a posthumous first-born, whose father could not redeem him on the thirtieth day after his birth, was supposed to carry a token around his neck to remind him to perform that formality for himself in due course. The medals issued from the close of the seventeenth century in London to the twelve "Jew Brokers" who alone were authorized to

---

* A token or jeton might be considered the link between a medal and a coin, since they are sometimes used as currency, but usually lack official sanction.

Brunswick, 1750.
Jeton: Silver, diam. 1⅜". FB 347.

Community tax on Shechita.
Koropka: Copper, diam. 1⁵⁄₁₆". FB 273.

Community tax on Shechita.
Koropka: Copper, diam. 1". FB 274.

[21]

practice on the Royal Exchange were vaguely in the same category as the membership tokens spoken of above, with one significant difference: the privilege was so highly valued—and so valuable—that a Jew Broker's medal sometimes cost as much as £5000 sterling.[*]

From the data assembled in the foregoing pages, it will have been realized that the history of the Jewish medal, taken in its broadest sense, embraces a wide range of Jewish history: artistic, political, biographical, organizational, charitable, economic, humanitarian. Even inconspicuous pieces of inscribed metal, with no aesthetic appeal or artistic merit whatsoever, may sometimes illustrate significant facets of the Jewish life in the past and throw light on the manner in which the Jew of the ghetto or the Pale of Settlement was able to regulate his life and to preserve the essential Jewish values.

Such medals and jetons (using the term in its wider sense) had already begun to engage the attention of certain European enthusiasts of an earlier generation, but for the most part only incidentally, as part of their general collections. The first person to devote himself specifically to this branch of collecting on a grand scale, and to develop the subject still further through his own efforts, was Samuel Friedenberg of New York, to whose collection and achievement this volume is devoted.

Name of individual, certifying his affiliation with a particular organization.

Jeton: Silver, engraved, 1⅛″ x ⅞″.
FB 339.

---

[*] Balloting tokens, often bearing the Hebrew "Yes" or "No" inscribed on small coins, are also not infrequently found in some countries.

In the *Rassegna Mensile di Israel XXVIII* (1962) pp. 377-388 is an article by U. Nahon on Italian-Jewish medals, with illustrations showing twelve of them dated between 1848 and 1957. An article on the medal production of Paul Vincze, much of whose work has been of Jewish inspiration, appeared in *The Studio* (October, 1962).

II

SAMUEL FRIEDENBERG symbolizes a type of the American Jew of his generation, his modest figure thus acquiring some historical significance. Born in 1886 at Schrenzck in Poland, then under Czarist rule, he was taken by his mother as a child of seven to New York, where his father had already established himself four years previously. He had the normal education of a New York Jewish boy of that period, first at public school and then at evening high school, which he supplemented by voracious reading. By 1907 he had entered into a business and became so successful that within a few years he had a controlling interest in two firms servicing the textile industry. In 1919 he sold out on favorable terms and entered the real estate business, building and owning a number of important commercial and residential structures in New York over the next decades.

But notwithstanding his increasing economic responsibilities and his many activities in Jewish philanthropic and communal work, he retained the cultural interests which he had developed in youth—no doubt inherited from generations of scholarly ancestors. Moreover, he had the collector's instinct—a quality with which a man is born, for it cannot be made. He belonged to a number of learned societies. He was a subscriber to the Metropolitan Museum of Art. He was enrolled as a "Benefactor" of the New York Botanical Gardens, the highest category of recognition accorded by that body. He was interested in prints and engravings, donating a large collection to the Brooklyn Museum.

Samuel Friedenberg himself described the genesis of his Jewish collection. Fairly early in his career he became interested in numismatics, and brought together a relatively important collection of United States coins. Inevitably, he knew, and had some knowledge about, the ancient Jewish coinage, and even had a few specimens, casually acquired, in his collection. But this is a specialized branch of the subject and did not engage his attention specifically.

It happened, however, that one day in 1935, shortly after the beginning of the Nazi persecution of the Jews, a refugee from Germany came to see him bringing a small package under his arm. "You are interested in numismatics, I believe," he said. "If so, I have something to show you." For a charitably inclined person at this time refusal was impossible, even if he had not been a collector. The stranger opened the package and revealed a cardboard shoe-box, containing forty-two medals, in silver or bronze, each one individually wrapped—a miscellaneous collection formed by his grandfather. Of the number, fifteen were inscribed in Hebrew or were otherwise of obvious Jewish interest.

This determined Samuel Friedenberg, even if he had any hesitancy at first, to buy what was offered to him; and the purchase changed the tenor of his life. It is one thing to know academically of the existence of a category of material, it is something different—more vivid and concrete— to handle examples, and even more so to own them. And now he owned not one or two specimens, but an important collection, modest in size, but so important that Alexander Marx, the great librarian of The Jewish Theological Seminary of America,* who knew everything that there was to know about Jewish collections and collecting, emphasized the rarity of what he had acquired.

Samuel Friedenberg was so impressed that, in effect, he now gave up his other branches of collecting and concentrated on the Jewish side alone. He became imbued with the thought of creating in America a new type of encyclopedia in metal, visible to all, so that it should be possible to see, as well as to read, a record of the accomplishments and contributions of the Jewish people. He studied, he purchased, he traveled, he compared, he wrote to dealers, he put himself in touch with collectors. And the little initial collection of fifteen pieces speedily grew, important items being added to it weekly, sometimes even daily.

But he did not interest himself only in the monumental pieces of major historical significance and artistic merit. *L'appétit vint en mangeant,* and from the widow of Benjamin Mintz, long the head of the Jewish National Fund in Warsaw and an outstanding connoisseur of Jewish art, he acquired a series of no fewer than 225 jetons and tokens of the type described above, illustrating the communal organization of Polish Jewry as a whole over several generations. Thus a new category of the collection was opened up. In due course, so as to round off his treatment of the subject, Samuel Friedenberg purchased from a fellow-collector a nearly complete corpus consisting of some 300 ancient Jewish coins and added it to the Friedenberg Collection, thus as it were reverting to the numismatic interest which had been his point of departure.

This was, unhappily, a favorable moment for the American collector. It was the period when the Nazi persecution in Europe was reaching its climax. Not only was important material being brought to the United States and elsewhere, sometimes surreptitiously (for the German authorities had now begun to strip their victims of all they possessed before driving them out), but public collections built up by the devotion of generations of collectors were being liquidated or in some cases destroyed by the heroes of the swastika. The acquisition of materials from Germany (and later on from some of the German-occupied countries) sometimes gave solid and important help to persons who had escaped and were trying to realize enough capital to exist or to start work again in a new land. Samuel Friedenberg was not the man to take unfair advantage of such

---

* See biography section, p. 44.

opportunities, and paid always at, or above, the market rate. There could be no question for him of profiting from another's desperation. He once described how after business hours he would sit in his office examining his new acquisitions and think, not only of their history and teaching, but also of the tragedy that had overwhelmed their former owners. On one occasion, a parcel came containing a number of interesting pieces along with an anonymous card which fortunately had escaped the German postal authorities, saying that the owner would rather he had the contents than the Nazis. It was many weeks afterwards that he heard from, and was able to compensate, the former possessor, who succeeded in leaving Germany.

In due course, Samuel Friedenberg decided to go to Europe himself in the summer of 1938. He made some important acquisitions but did not have the heart to go into Germany, so that his thirst remained unsatisfied. At one time, he had the idea of advertising in the German newspapers for objects for his collection, but was advised that under one of the recent demented regulations no general periodical would accept any advertisement inserted by a Jew or a Jewish firm. No alternative seemed left except to enter Germany himself, however reluctant he might feel, and see what could be snatched from the maelstrom. In the summer of 1939, while the war clouds were gathering, he crossed the Atlantic again and went straight to Germany—no mean act of courage then, when the Nazis were relentlessly engaged in suppressing the last remnant of German Jewish life that had thus far survived.

His first objective was the ancient city of Frankfurt-am-Main, always an important center for connoisseurs of Jewish books and objets d'art. This place was especially important in his case since the remarkable medal collection of Dr. Otto Goldschmidt of Gotha, the finest of the type in Germany, numbering over 450 separate specimens, had been placed on loan in the Frankfurt Jewish Museum after the owner's death not long before. But the Museum had been closed by the Nazis following the brutal night of destruction of November 9, 1938, the "Kristallnacht," when synagogues by the hundred were burned down throughout the country and tens of thousands of persons were thrown into concentration camps. Though he was advised never to stray from the main streets of the town if he went out because of the perpetual danger that a Jew now incurred if recognized, Samuel Friedenberg had the courage to open negotiations through an intermediary with the Gestapo to purchase the entire collection. But the atmosphere became increasingly forbidding. The intermediary was visited by the police, and Mr. Friedenberg gave up the attempt and left the city.

At Vienna, conditions were as bad as at Frankfurt. The city was under the Nazi jackboot, and those dealers and collectors with whom he had been in touch concerning his collection in former days could no longer even be traced. Budapest, where he rejoined Mrs. Friedenberg (who had been naturally reluctant to travel to Germany with him), came as a welcome relief, though the condition of the Jews was deteriorating. But nothing could be acquired there, and even in Poland, at Cracow and Warsaw, no medals of any significance were available, a testimony itself to the thoroughness of the previous inquiries and the completeness which the collection had attained in only four or five years. In mid-August, Mr. and Mrs. Friedenberg returned to New York—just in time, since war broke out a couple of weeks later.

There was to be a sequel to this adventurous trip. Well after the conclusion of hostilities, in 1951, Dr. Guido Schoenberger, at one time curator of the Jewish Museum in Frankfurt, who had subsequently settled in the United States, went back to Germany on behalf of the Jewish Cultural Reconstruction, Inc., with United States government authority and support. His mission had as its principal object to recover the former Jewish Museum collection, which had simply been transferred in 1939 to the Historical Museum of Frankfurt. Mr. Friedenberg cabled to remind him of the Goldschmidt medal collection. Dr. Schoenberger began inquiries and found that the collection had been deposited with the Coin and Medal Section at the Frankfurt Stadtbibliothek. A problem existed in that, technically, these objects did not belong to the Jewish Museum (with which they had only been deposited) but to private individuals, then untraceable. Nevertheless, Dr. Schoenberger managed to have the medal collection declared an integral part of the Frankfurt Jewish Museum. It was accordingly brought back to the United States, with the bulk of the former Museum collection.

But the problem was not settled even then. The legal owners had to be found, for Dr. Goldschmidt's direct heir, who had left the collection in Frankfurt, was dead. It was some time before his heirs could be traced— one in South Africa, and one in England. Ultimately the negotiations were completed, and Mr. Friedenberg bought the collection from them. Nearly 200 pieces were found to be already in his catalogue and were therefore presented to the Bezalel Museum in Jerusalem, where the Samuel Friedenberg Collection now constitutes a special section. But no fewer than 247 were new and, when added to his main collection, made it incomparably the greatest of its type in the world.

By now, however, the collection was no longer physically in his hands. In one respect Samuel Friedenberg was unlike most other art connoisseurs. His passion was that of the collector, not of the possessor, and he regarded his collecting as a public service rather than a private indulgence. Accordingly, when his collection had attained importance he considered that its proper place was not in his own home, but in some place where it could be accessible to the general public. The obvious destination was New York, specifically the Jewish Museum of The Jewish Theological Seminary of America, which in 1947, under the direction of Dr. Stephen S. Kayser, had taken on renewed vigor when it had been transferred to the former Warburg mansion at the corner of Fifth Avenue and 92nd Street. In 1950, therefore, Mr. Friedenberg made over the entire collection as an absolute gift to the Jewish Museum, where it is displayed in a special room.

But his interest in the collection was in no way abated, and almost to the day of his death in 1957 he continued to add specimens. In the end, in addition to hundreds of tokens and jetons of various sorts, no fewer than 353 medals celebrating memorable events in Jewish history, and over 700 commemorating important personalities in Jewish life, were included in the collection. Not all of these, however, were old, for in the last decade the owner had begun to think of his collection and its development in a new light.

Already at the time of the outbreak of World War II, in the autumn of 1939, a large proportion of the 500 pieces (apart from jetons) which the Friedenberg Collection of medals then numbered, were, as has been indicated, portrait-medals, signalizing persons of great significance in Jewish history, such as Moses Mendelssohn, Moses Montefiore, Adolphe Crémieux, and Theodor Herzl. It was in fact, as Samuel Friedenberg viewed it, a graphic record of all Jewish achievement in the western world, executed in metal.

Yet it was manifestly incomplete. There were some medals which, despite all his efforts, he had been unable to trace. Though many outstanding Jews had been portrayed in this manner in the past, others had not. Moreover, there were many contemporaries whose contribution to humanity was considerable but who as yet had not been signalized in this medium. And so an idea of genius grew on Samuel Friedenberg. Why not complete the collection by commissioning an additional series of such medals, which would fill in the gaps and bring it up to date? More than one purpose would be served by this. It would round off the Friedenberg Collection of medals. It would give a stimulus to the art of the medalist. And, above all, it would complete a series of representations, of high artistic merit in themselves, which would show graphically, in metal, the features of the Jews who had made outstanding contributions to human culture and western life, whether in art, music, politics, literature, medicine, philanthropy, or the humanities. Here would be, conceived in bronze, a Jewish Hall of Fame, which would convey impressively to those who viewed it an idea of what this small group of maligned people, then being systematically hounded down and exterminated by the Nazi thugs throughout Europe, had achieved for human civilization.

Samuel Friedenberg threw himself into the enlarging of the collection with the same enthusiasm as he had devoted to forming it in the first instance. He began by drawing up preliminary lists of names of Jews who had contributed to human endeavor in every walk of life, a task necessitating long and patient research. With the aid of such scholars as Alexander Marx, Abraham Neuman, Barry Schneiderman, and Julian Morgenstern, the lists were supplemented and perfected. Characteristic of the man was that he included not only the names of Jews who had won acclaim in the outside world, but also those modest scholars, philanthropists, and public workers who had self-sacrificingly and unostentatiously devoted themselves to the betterment of Jewish life and the forwarding of Jewish culture.

The problem of fabricating the medals remained. For this, too, no trouble and no expenditure were spared. He commissioned a series of medalists of high reputation to carry out the work for him in various lands. In the United States, these included Ivan Sors (Stern), C. Paolo, J. Hovell, and A. Eisenberg; and in England, F. J. Kormis and Benno Elkan. In most instances, only a single medal was made, the original plaster cast being destroyed. Thus the specimen in the Friedenberg Collection is unique.

In the case of persons belonging to the past (such as Menasseh ben Israel, to cite only one example), old portraits and engravings were traced and translated into bronze. Contemporaries were almost always modeled from life. Everywhere the greatest interest was aroused, and enthusiastic collaboration was forthcoming. Leslie Hore-Belisha, former British Minister for War, who gave sittings to Kormis, wrote to Mr. Friedenberg on November 17, 1941, on House of Commons stationery: "I can know of no idea better calculated to inspire the oncoming generation of Jewry than to make others realize what has been contributed to the world by a people numerically so small." And there were others, such as the present writer, who felt when they received this flattering invitation that here was an appreciation of their work which could only have come from a person imbued with a sense of Jewish cultural values.

Some 700 medals in all were commissioned or acquired by Samuel Friedenberg. Of these, approximately 200 are reproduced in this volume. Thus we have here, if not the full Hall of Fame quite as Samuel Friedenberg conceived it, at least what might be termed the Inner Hall, comprising the effigies in metal of some of those who made a major contribution to civilization and culture. It is a picture gallery of Jewish history. It is a monument to Jewish genius. It is in part a remarkable assembly of the productions of some great Jewish plastic artists. It is a collection of works of art in metal, memorable often for their own sake. But above all it is a memorial to the enthusiasm, taste, and particular genius of the man who created it—Samuel Friedenberg.

BIBLIOGRAPHY

W. Ahrens, *Hebräische Amuelette mit magischen Zahlenquadraten,* Berlin (1916).
S. Ferares, "La médaille dite de Fourvières et sa légende hébraïque," *Revue numismatique,* 196 (1910).
M. Goldstein and K. Dreadner, *Kultura i Sztuka Ludu żydowskiego na Ziemiach Polskich,* Warsaw (1935).
T. Hoffmann, *Jacob Abraham und Abraham Abrahamson—55 Jahre Medaillenkunst 1755–1810,* Frankfurt-am-Main (1927).
B. Kisch, "Jewish Community Tokens," *Historia Judaica,* xv (1953).
———, "Judaica in Numnis," *ibid.,* vii, 135-58 (1945).
———, "Shekel Medals and False Shekels," *ibid.,* iii (1941).
E. Pariset, "La médaille énigmatique," *Mémoires de l'Académie des Sciences de Lyon,* ix, 87ff. (1907).
A. Polak, *Joodse penningen in de Nederland,* Amsterdam (1958).

Philosophy
&
Religion

GREAT JEWISH PORTRAITS IN METAL

ISAAC da FONSECA ABOAB (1605-1693)

Born Castrodaire, Portugal; died Amsterdam, Holland. Rabbi.
PLAQUE: *Cast bronze, 4¾″ x 4″, by I. Sors. FB 479.*

Fleeing from the Inquisition, Isaac Aboab was taken by his family to Amsterdam in 1612. He studied there under the noted scholar, Isaac Uzziel, and, at age twenty-one, became rabbi of a large congregation. In 1639 three congregations united and Aboab was named rabbi, but he relinquished this post to accept a call to a newly formed congregation in Pernambuco, Brazil, where he became the first rabbi and Jewish author in the New World (1642). In 1649, however, war between Holland and Portugal resulted in Portuguese possession of Brazil and the expulsion of the Jews. Aboab returned to Amsterdam and was immediately reinstated as rabbi of his former congregation. Learned in philosophy and science, he was a gifted orator and writer and inspired the erection of the magnificent synagogue in Amsterdam.

ISRAEL ABRAHAMS (1858-1925)

Born London, England; died Cambridge, England. Scholar.
PLAQUE: *Cast bronze, 4⅛″ x 5″, by Kormis. FB 864.*

Israel Abrahams was educated at Jews' College and University College, and received his M.A. from the University of London in 1881. He taught at Jews' College and in 1902 became reader in rabbinic and Talmudic literature at the University of Cambridge. The foremost Anglo-Jewish scholar of his time, Abrahams was co-editor of the *Jewish Quarterly Review* (1889-1908) and raised that periodical to a position of international preëminence. He has also been credited with playing perhaps the major role in the great growth in knowledge of the Hebrew language during the first quarter of the twentieth century. Abrahams was a founder of the Jewish Historical Society of England, honorary president of the University of Glasgow Theological Society, and president of the Society of Historical Theology at Oxford. Among his many works are *Aspects of Judaism* (1895), *Jewish Life in the Middle Ages* (1896), *Chapters in Jewish Literature* (1898), and *A Short History of Jewish Literature* (1906).

DON ISAAC ABRAVANEL (1437-1508)

Born Lisbon, Portugal; died Venice, Italy. Statesman, philosopher, and Biblical exegete.
PLAQUE: *Cast bronze, 4³⁄₁₆″ x 3½″, by I. Sors. FB 618.*

Last of an illustrious family of the Spanish Golden Age, Isaac Abravanel was treasurer to King Alfonso V of Portugal and one of that monarch's most trusted advisers. He was dismissed by King John II in 1483, however, and fled to Castile, where he entered the service of Ferdinand and Isabella. An unstinting philanthropist, he gave and solicited money in order to obtain the freedom of Moroccan Jews enslaved by the Moors and, when the Jews were banished from

Spain, offered to pay the king an enormous sum in return for the revocation of the edict. His offer was refused and he departed Castile for Italy, where he served the Neopolitan king until the fall of Naples in 1495. He found refuge in Venice eight years later. Abravanel was a superb scholar whose Biblical exegesis exerted great influence on seventeenth- and eighteenth-century scholarship. He is known, too, for his philosophy and for his brilliant defense of the messianic doctrine.

CYRUS ADLER (1863-1940)

Born Van Buren, Arkansas; died New York City. Orientalist, educator, and historian.
PLAQUE: *Cast bronze, 6⅛" x 4¾", by Mantel. FB 616.*

After receiving his Ph.D. from Johns Hopkins University (1887), Cyrus Adler remained there as a professor of Semitic languages until 1893. On the staffs of the United States National Museum and the Smithsonian Institution, he was called to the presidency of Dropsie College for Hebrew and Cognate Learning in 1908. Later he was acting president of The Jewish Theological Seminary of America (1916-24) and president from 1924 until his death. In 1888 he helped to found the Jewish Publication Society and was chairman of the board for the preparation of its translation of the Bible (1908-15). He headed the departments of post-Biblical antiquities and Jews of America for the *Jewish Encyclopedia*. Editor of the *Jewish Quarterly Review* and a president of the American Jewish Committee, he was also a member of numerous learned societies. As a representative at the Versailles Peace Conference (1919) he sponsored the inclusion of minority rights clauses in treaties with new states. In 1901 he published, together with I. M. Casanowicz, a "Descriptive Catalogue of a Collection of Objects of Jewish Ceremonial Deposited in the U. S. National Museum by Jadji Ephraim Benguiat" (now part of the Jewish Museum of The Jewish Theological Seminary).

NATHAN MARCUS ADLER (1803-1890)

Born Hanover, Germany; died Brighton, England. Rabbi.
PLAQUE: *Cast bronze, 4½" x 3¹¹⁄₁₆", by Kormis. FB 620.*

Nathan Marcus Adler received his Ph.D. from the University of Erlangen in 1828 and became Chief Rabbi of Oldenburg the following year. He later served in the same capacity in Hanover (1830-45) and in London (1845-90). In the latter city, Adler founded the famous Jews' College (1855) and was its first president. Five years later he proposed the establishment of a United Synagogue, which would combine all British congregations under one central administration. This suggestion was realized when Parliament passed the United Synagogue Act of 1870. One of the truly great orthodox rabbis of his day, Adler was the author of *Nethinah La-ger* (*A Gift to the Proselyte*, 1875), a brilliant commentary on Onkelos's paraphrastic translation of the Bible into Aramaic.

AHAD HA-AM (ASHER GINZBERG) (1856-1927)

Born Skvira, Russia; died Tel-Aviv, Palestine. Essayist and philosopher.
PLAQUE: *Cast bronze, 5⅜" x 4⅛", by I. Sors. FB 565.*

Asher Ginzberg studied in Vienna, Berlin, and Breslau (1876-85). Writing under the pseudonym Ahad Ha-am ("one of the people") he was the foremost Jewish philosophical essayist of his day. He stood firmly opposed to Theodor Herzl's political Zionism and advocated in its stead a "spiritual Zionism." Ahad Ha-am asserted that ethics are a national rather than a sociological phenomenon, and he demanded the education of the Jews so that they might be prepared to accept their nationality and make of their homeland a spiritual center creatively influencing Jews of the Diaspora. Dismayed at what he considered Zionism's hasty methods, he claimed it to be far less important that people go to Palestine than that they know *why* they are going. Ahad Ha-am was editor of the Hebrew monthly *Hashiloach*. His collected essays were published as *At the Crossroads* (four volumes, 1895).

ZEBI HIRSCH ASHKENAZI (1658-1718)

Born Moravia, Austria; died Lemberg, Poland. Rabbi and Talmudist.
PLAQUE: *Cast bronze, 4¹¹⁄₁₆" x 3¾", by Mantel. FB 766.*

After years of travel and study, Zebi Ashkenazi assumed the position of rabbi of Sarajevo in 1686. Four years later he was called to Altona, where he served as rabbi of a Klaus (a school and retreat for students of the Talmud) and, for a time, as a congregational rabbi. Having witnessed in his travels the enormity of the schism caused by Sabbatai Zevi's messianic heresy, Ashkenazi soon found himself engulfed in the very feud that he himself most deplored. In 1690 he accepted the post of Ashkenazic rabbi of Amsterdam, where, having excommunicated a well-known Sephardic Sabbataian, he became the center of a very bitter Sephardic-Ashkenazic quarrel. Not until he went to Lemberg in 1717 did he find the peace that he so much desired. A truly great intellect, Ashkenazi was one of the most renowned scholars of his day. A collection of his responsa was published in 1712.

LEO BAECK (1874-1956)

Born Posen, Germany; died London, England. Rabbi and theologian.
PLAQUE: *Cast bronze, 5³⁄₁₆" x 4¾", by I. Sors. FB 794.*

Son of Rabbi Samuel Baeck, one of the most distinguished Jewish historians of the nineteenth century, Leo Baeck was educated at the Academy for the Science of Judaism in Berlin. He served as rabbi in Oppeln, Düsseldorf, and, after 1912, in Berlin. A prominent figure in German Liberal Judaism, Baeck became head of the Central Council of German Jews in 1933, retaining that post until the Nazi liquidation of the German Jewish community. After spending two years in Theresienstadt concentration camp (1943-45), he was liberated by the Allies and thereupon settled in London. Baeck believed Judaism to be the supreme expression of morality; he maintained that the essence of Judaism, contained in its God-concept and moral commands, is eternal and immutable, although Judaism's ceremonial forms are transient and subject to constant change. Among his writings are *The Essence of Judaism* (1905) and *The Pharisees and Other Essays* (1934).

HENRI BERGSON (1859-1941)

Born and died Paris, France. Philosopher.
MEDAL: *Cast bronze, 2¾" x 1¹⁵⁄₁₆", by H. Kautsch. FB 26.*

Henri Bergson's philosophy contradicted popular nineteenth-century Hegelianism, which had insisted that knowledge was attainable only through intellectual processes. Bergson viewed life as having two opposing tendencies: change and duration. Man knows change through the intellect, which views the universe scientifically, separating things from one another and categorizing them. But above intellect, Bergson felt, is intuition, which perceives *all* of life in its continual process of becoming. The intellect sees time as change; intuition sees time as duration, a point demonstrated by the act of memory. His ideas concerning time and memory directly influenced Marcel Proust, whose *Remembrance of Things Past* is based in large part upon this philosophy. Bergson was professor of philosophy at the Collège de France, a member of the French Academy, and recipient of the 1927 Nobel Prize for literature. Among his many works are *Time and Free Will* (1888), *Matter and Memory* (1896), and *Creative Evolution* (1907).

MARTIN BUBER (1878-   )

Born Vienna, Austria. Religious philosopher and scholar.
PLAQUE: *Cast bronze, 6⁷⁄₁₆" x 4¹⁄₁₆", by I. Sors. FB 860.*

Martin Buber studied at the Universities of Vienna, Leipzig, Berlin, and Zürich (1896-1900). At the University of Frankfurt from 1923 to 1933 he occupied the only chair of Jewish philosophy of religion and ethics in all of Germany. He was an advocate of the pioneer colonization of Palestine and participated in numerous Zionist congresses, always urging friendliness toward the Arabs. An active political Zionist for most of his life and the editor of several German Jewish periodicals, he was exiled after the rise of Hitler. In 1938 Buber became professor of social philosophy at the Hebrew University in Jerusalem. His religious approach, greatly influenced by Hasidic mysticism, conceives of faith as a dialogue between man and God. Buber is one of the leading theologians of the twentieth century and the author of many varied works, including *I and Thou* (1923) and *Tales of the Hasidim* (1928).

ZEVI HIRSCH ben MEIR CHAJES (1805-1855)

Born Brody, Poland; died Lemberg, Poland. Rabbi and Talmudist.
PLAQUE: *Cast bronze, 3⁵⁄₁₆" x 4¹⁵⁄₁₆", by I. Sors. FB 641.*

Zevi Chajes is said to have been totally familiar with the Bible at the age of five. Whether this is true or not, it *is* known that he received an excellent Jewish and secular education and that in 1828 he became rabbi of Zólkiew, where he officiated during most of his life. Through his pioneer efforts in the scientific study of Judaism he helped to pave the way for the great nineteenth- and twentieth-century investigations in that field. There are few modern works on Halakhah or Aggadah that do not depend at least in part upon his original studies. His *Torah Nebiim* (1836) was a defense of the validity of Talmudic tradition, and his excellent *Introduction to the Talmud* (1845) was an exposition of Talmudic methodology. Among his many other publications were books on Maimonides, Rashi, Jewish history, and Jewish law.

[33]

HERMANN COHEN (1842-1918)

Born Coswig, Germany; died Berlin, Germany. Philosopher.
PLAQUE: *Cast bronze, 4⁷⁄₁₆″ x 6″, by I. Sors. FB 1018.*

Hermann Cohen was educated at the Breslau Seminary and at the Universities of Breslau, Berlin, and Halle. He later taught at the University of Marburg (1873-1912). The most prominent representative of the neo-Kantian school of philosophy, Cohen sought to construct a system of knowledge that would be based entirely on logic. He separated logic (the problem of what *is*) from ethics (the problem of what *ought to be*), claiming that this was the only way in which answers could be arrived at. His ethical teachings were based entirely on Judaism, for he felt that the Jewish moral laws constituted a perfect system and thus could not be improved upon. The three major works in which Cohen propounded his philosophy are *The Logic of Pure Knowledge* (1902), *The Ethic of the Pure Will* (1904), and *The Aesthetic of Pure Feeling* (1912).

JAMES DARMESTETER (1849-1894)

Born Château-Salins, France; died Paris, France. Orientalist.
PLAQUE: *Cast bronze, 4⅝″ x 3¹³⁄₁₆″, by I. Sors. FB 648.*

A brilliant student, James Darmesteter entered the École des Hautes Études in 1872 and within three years had become a teacher there. A collection of his essays, *Iranian Studies*, appeared in 1883, and in 1886 he was appointed professor of Iranian languages at the Collège de France. He was recipient of a prize of 20,000 francs for his exceptionally fine translation of the Persian *Zend-Avesta*. Editor of *La Revue de Paris*, he was also the author of works on Persian poetry and Afghan folk music, and of *The Prophets of Israel* (1892), in which he argued that monotheism and messianism were Judaism's greatest contributions to civilization. Earlier, he had been the first to point out the enormous influence of the Bible and neo-Platonism on Zoroastrianism. Not confining himself to oriental studies, however, Darmesteter also wrote excellent studies on Shakespeare and English literature and was the editor of several texts of English classics.

SIMON MARKEVICH DUBNOW (1860-1941)

Born Mstislavl, Russia; died Riga, Russia. Historian.
PLAQUE: *Cast bronze, 4⁷⁄₁₆″ x 3⅜″, by I. Sors. FB 593.*

Simon Dubnow, author of the ten-volume *General History of the Jewish People* (1901), held to a sociological conception of history and firmly believed that the Jews were an historically and culturally autonomous group. They form, he contended, not a state within a state, but a nation among nations, aiming at cultural rather than political autonomy. He once wrote that the "... spiritual powers of the Jewish people and their unity were preserved by the organized Jewish community during the two thousand years of their dispersion." Dubnow was an immensely popular writer, whose method marked a definite turning point in Jewish historiography with its sociological, rather than purely spiritual, approach.

SIMON M. DUBNOW

1860

AKIBA EGER, The Younger (1761-1837)

Born Eisenstadt, Hungary; died Posen, Germany. Rabbi and Talmudist.
PLAQUE: *Cast zinc, 5¼″ x 3⅞″, by I. Sors. FB 655.*

Akiba Eger, grandson of the illustrious scholar of the same name, was rabbi in Märkish Friedland, West Prussia (1791-1815), when he was called to Posen. An unyielding opponent of reform in Judaism, he insisted that any alteration of rabbinic Judaism would bring the Torah to destruction. Although he demanded strict adherence to law, he nonetheless advocated leniency in cases of illness or emergency. He demonstrated his great humanitarianism during the cholera epidemic of 1831 when his every day and night were spent in bringing comfort to the suffering. Eger was a great Talmudic scholar and produced numerous responsa and glosses on rabbinic texts. On the centennial of his death an Eger Museum was established in Eisenstadt to honor his memory.

ELIJAH ben SOLOMON, Gaon of Vilna (1720-1797)

Born and died Vilna, Lithuania. Scholar.
PLAQUE: *Cast bronze, 6⅜16″ x 4⅛″, by I. Sors. FB 656.*

Elijah ben Solomon was a wandering student until he returned to Vilna in 1748, already recognized as a sage. He was a man of great gentleness, who preferred to teach in small groups so that his students might better imbibe the fullness of Jewish knowledge. The Gaon of Vilna applied the science of philology to the Talmud and, by his method of internal criticism, opened the door to future scientific investigations into religious works. Scarcely any subject evaded his inquiry—Hebrew grammar, Bible, Mishnah (all generally overlooked by Talmudists before him). Singlehandedly he awakened interest in the long-neglected Palestinian Talmud. The Gaon was the first Jewish scholar to insist upon the importance of secular knowledge, asserting that mathematics, astronomy, and anatomy were indispensable to real comprehension of the Talmud. He was the author of commentaries on almost every major Hebrew religious work.

JONATHAN EYBESCHÜTZ (1690-1764)

Born Cracow, Poland; died Altona, Germany. Rabbi and Talmudist.
PLAQUE: *Cast bronze, 5⅜16″ x 3¹¹⁄16″, by I. Sors. FB 558.*

After years of study in Prossnitz, Vienna, and Hamburg, Jonathan Eybeschütz settled in Prague in 1714, achieving great success as head of a yeshiva. In 1725, however, he was denounced for his cabalistic tendencies and, most particularly, for his alleged sympathy with the messianic heresy of Sabbatai Zevi. Never fully vindicated, Eybeschütz spent the following thirty years under the threat of renewed accusations. First in Metz (where he was called in 1741) and later in Altona (as Chief Rabbi of Altona, Hamburg, and Wandsbeck, 1750-64), he fought constantly to protect himself from his persecutors. Ever respected as a scholar, in 1755 he wrote his *Tablets of the Testimony,* a brilliant rebuttal to those who would discredit him, in which were included testimonials from numerous important men of the day. Thereafter he was allowed to live in peace. One of the most loved and most hated men in Jewish history, Eybeschütz has never ceased to be a subject of controversy.

ABRAHAM FLEXNER (1866-1959)

Born Louisville, Kentucky; died Falls Church, Virginia. Educational reformer.
PLAQUE: *Cast bronze, 5" x 3¾", by I. Sors. FB 659.*

Abraham Flexner was educated at Johns Hopkins University, Harvard University, and the University of Berlin. He met great success with his own experimental preparatory school in Louisville and in 1910 published a condemnatory report entitled *Medical Education in the United States and Canada.* This study led to immediate reforms in teaching methods, curricula, and laboratory facilities in medical schools in America and Europe. He later questioned the entire American educational system in *A Modern School* (1916) and *A Modern College* (1923). Flexner was an executive of the General Education Board of the Rockefeller Foundation (1913-28), and his work soon convinced John D. Rockefeller, Sr. to donate $50,000,000 toward the realization of his reform measures. Flexner personally raised the money for the Institute for Advanced Study at Princeton, New Jersey, organized it, and was its first director (1930-39). One of the most able and successful educational reformers of our time, he was the brother of Simon Flexner, the eminent pathologist.

ZACHARIAS FRANKEL (1801-1875)

Born Prague, Bohemia; died Breslau, Germany. Rabbi and educator.
PLAQUE: *Cast bronze, 5" x 3⅞", by I. Sors. FB 573.*

Shortly after his graduation from the University of Budapest, Zacharias Frankel was appointed rabbi at Teplitz. There he introduced organ music into the service and was the first rabbi in Bohemia to preach in German. In 1836 he became Chief Rabbi of Dresden. Frankel was attacked by Orthodox Jews for permitting free research into traditional Jewish sources and by Reform Jews for his adherence to ritual. It was partly in light of his median position between these two movements that he was chosen director of the Breslau Rabbinical Seminary when it opened (1854), lest the school become an organ either of reform or of orthodoxy. He continued to serve as its director until his death. Known today as the first Conservative Jew, Frankel was a brilliant scholar whose finest works are his *Introduction to the Mishnah* (1859), a systematic history of rabbinical literature and theology, and his *Introduction to the Palestinian Talmud* (1870).

ABRAHAM GEIGER (1810-1874)

Born Frankfurt-am-Main, Germany; died Berlin, Germany. Rabbi.
PLAQUE: *Cast bronze, 6¾" x 5¼", by Paolo. FB 605.*

While rabbi in Wiesbaden, Abraham Geiger called the first assembly of rabbis inclined toward liberalism (1837) and thereafter was the acknowledged leader of Reform Judaism. In 1840 he became second rabbi of Breslau and first rabbi three years later. His revolutionary ideas, however, caused a split in the congregation: he rejected the doctrine of a personal Messiah, conducted services in the vernacular, and omitted all prayers for the return to Zion and the rebuilding of the Temple. In 1854 he published his *Israelite Prayerbook*, which embodied these and other Reform Jewish principles. Called to Frankfurt-am-Main in 1863, Geiger served in Berlin after 1870 and was on the original faculty of the Academy for the Science of Judaism (1872-74). He was founder and editor of two scholarly journals and an eager exponent of the scientific approach to Jewish studies. His own brilliant scholarship gave great and badly needed strength to Reform Judaism in its early days.

LOUIS GINZBERG (1873-1953)

Born Kovno, Lithuania; died New York City. Scholar and educator.
PLAQUE: *Cast bronze, 5⅛" x 4⅜", by I. Sors. FB 1005.*

Louis Ginzberg studied at the Universities of Berlin, Strasbourg, and Heidelberg, receiving his Ph.D. from the latter institution in 1898. He came to the United States the following year and in 1902 became professor of Talmud and rabbinics at The Jewish Theological Seminary of America. Ginzberg wrote extensively on the Gaonic period and the Palestinian Talmud and was editor of the department of rabbinic literature of the *Jewish Encyclopedia.* Among his works are *Students, Scholars, and Saints* (1928) and *A Commentary on the Palestinian Talmud* (three volumes, 1941), in which he traced the development of the ritual, the liturgy, and rabbinic theology. His brilliant work on the Aggadah, *The Legends of the Jews* (six volumes, 1909-28), remains a standard work in that field. Ginzberg was one of the most profound and literate scholars of the twentieth century and the recipient of many honorary degrees.

AARON DAVID GORDON (1856-1922)

Born Troyanov, Russia; died Dagania, Palestine. Philosopher.
PLAQUE: *Cast bronze, 5¾6" x 3¹⁵⁄₁₆", by I. Sors. FB 665.*

Aaron David Gordon, an enthusiastic Zionist, migrated to Palestine in 1904 and there became a manual laborer. He was a neo-romantic who decried man's alienation from the soil and gradual loss of individuality. His philosophy (*Am-Adam*) asserted that a people is regenerated through its individuals and that work alone can effect this regeneration by giving man roots and permitting him to grow. Gordon's ideas had a great influence on the labor movement in Palestine and have served almost as a watchword in the *kibbutzim.* In the international realm, Gordon asserted that for all practical purposes two nations are the same as two individuals; in both instances there is inherent the duty to cooperate for the good of both parties. Gordon's theories were well received both in his own country and in Europe, where he was known through his writings: *The Religion of Work* and *Letters from Palestine,* among others.

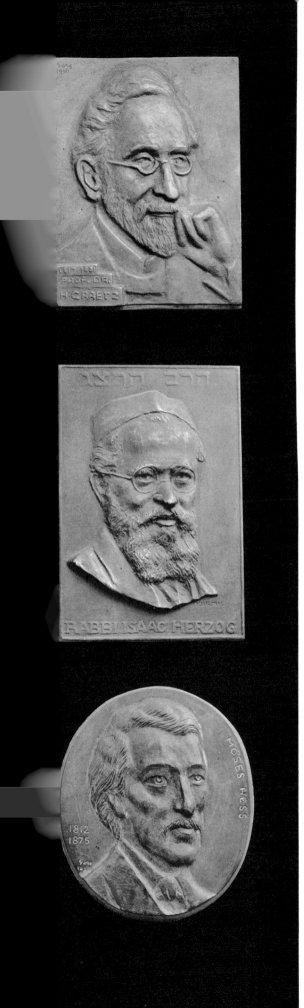

HEINRICH GRAETZ (1817-1891)

Born Posen, Germany; died Munich, Germany. Historian.
PLAQUE: *Cast bronze, 6" x 4⅝", by I. Sors. FB 451.*

From 1837 to 1840 Heinrich Graetz lived and worked with Samson Raphael Hirsch, the great leader of Orthodox Judaism. He later studied and taught in various parts of Germany and was appointed professor of history and Biblical exegesis at the Breslau Seminary (1854-91) and at the University of Breslau (1869-91). Graetz's fame rests primarily upon his eleven-volume *History of the Jews* (1853-75), one of the most brilliant and comprehensive studies ever attempted. Although distinctly biased in presentation, it was the first work to regard the entirety of Jewish history as a unit of truly heroic proportions progressing logically from its inception up to his time. Graetz was one of the most influential historians of all time and gained great popularity through his exciting narrative style and intense prosemitism. He was also the author of a number of exegetical works based on daring textual emendations.

ISAAC HALEVI HERZOG (1888-1959)

Born Lomza, Poland; died Jerusalem, Israel. Rabbi.
PLAQUE: *Cast bronze, 5½" x 3⅞", by Kormis. FB 450.*

Isaac Herzog studied at the Universities of Leeds, Paris, and London and was ordained a rabbi in 1910. Five years later he became rabbi of Belfast and was appointed Chief Rabbi of Dublin in 1919 and of the entire Irish Free State six years later. He declined an offer to serve as Chief Rabbi of Greece (1932) but could not refuse an appointment to the same position in Palestine when it was offered to him in 1936. During and after World War II the greater part of his time was devoted to the rescue and resettlement of European Jewry. Known throughout the world for his humanitarianism and scholarship, Herzog is the author of many learned works, of which the best known is perhaps *The Main Institutions of Jewish Law* (five volumes, 1936-39).

MOSES HESS (1812-1875)

Born Bonn, Germany; died Paris, France. Social philosopher.
PLAQUE: *Cast bronze, 4⁹⁄₁₆" x 4", by I. Sors. FB 512.*

Almost entirely self-educated, Moses Hess began his literary career as a journalist. After a short period in England he settled in Paris (1840) and, under the influence of Hegel and Spinoza, wrote *The European Triarchy* (1841), which outlined a plan for a United States of Europe. Hess soon became associated with Karl Marx and Friedrich Engels but was unable to accept their economic interpretation of history, insisting upon his own humanistic approach as found in his *Holy History of Humanity* (1837). He later devoted himself almost exclusively to the study of Jewish history and prepared the way for the Zionist movement with *Rome and Jerusalem* (1862). In this work he described the indestructibility of the Jewish people and argued that the Jews would always be aliens in Europe, no matter what the degree of their legal emancipation. Hess's answer to this dilemma was the colonization of Palestine. His argument profoundly influenced incipient Zionists of the nineteenth century.

SAMSON RAPHAEL HIRSCH (1808-1888)

Born Hamburg, Germany; died Frankfurt-am-Main, Germany. Rabbi.
PLAQUE: *Cast bronze, 4¹³⁄₁₆″ x 3½″, by I. Sors. FB 741.*

Samson Raphael Hirsch, the most literate defender of Orthodox
Judaism of modern times, served as rabbi in Oldenburg, Emden, and
Nikolsburg. In 1851 he was appointed rabbi of a separatist group
in Frankfurt-am-Main, which, under his leadership, became the center
of Orthodox Judaism in Germany. The founder of neo-orthodoxy,
Hirsch fought uncompromisingly against Reform Judaism, regarding
the difference between a Liberal and an Orthodox Jew as greater than
that between a Protestant and a Catholic. He contended that no
"reform" should go further than to give the ancient and immutable
laws and practices a deeper symbolic meaning. Hirsch was the author
of many scholarly religious works, among which his *Nineteen Letters
About Judaism* (1836), written in flawless, classical German, was the
first intellectual defense of orthodoxy. He also wrote a translation of,
and commentary on, the Pentateuch (1867-78).

EDMUND HUSSERL (1859-1938)

Born Prossnitz, Austria; died Freiburg, Germany. Philosopher.
PLAQUE: *Cast bronze, 5¼″ x 3⅝″, by I. Sors. FB 95.*

Edmund Husserl began work in the field of philosophy while completing his studies in mathematics in Vienna. In 1896, as a member
of the faculty of the University of Halle (1887-1901), he announced
his discovery of an entirely new field of philosophy: phenomenology.
Directed toward the description and definition of conscious data,
phenomenology asserts the intuitive basis of all knowledge and the
purposefulness of every conscious act. It concerns itself primarily
with an analysis of the relationship between the subjective ego and
the objective reality that it perceives. Husserl was one of the most
influential philosophers of our time and served as professor of philosophy at the Universities of Göttingen (1901-16) and Freiburg
(1916-28). He was the author of *Logical Analyses* (1900-01) and
Ideas Toward a Pure Phenomenology (1913).

MORDECAI MENAHEM KAPLAN (1881-   )

Born Swenziany, Lithuania. Rabbi, philosopher, and educator.
PLAQUE: *Cast bronze, 7⁵⁄₁₆″ x 5¹¹⁄₁₆″, by I. Sors. FB 839.*

A graduate of the City College of New York, Mordecai Kaplan was
ordained at The Jewish Theological Seminary of America in 1902.
In 1909, at the invitation of Solomon Schechter, he became the first
principal of the Seminary's Teachers Institute and, in 1930, professor
of homiletics and philosophy at the Seminary and dean of the Institute. In 1916 Rabbi Kaplan established the Jewish Center in New
York, the first synagogue center of its kind in the United States. His
Society for the Advancement of Judaism was organized in 1912 and its
famous journal, *The Reconstructionist,* began publication thirteen
years later. Reconstructionism, the philosophy expounded by Kaplan,
maintains that Judaism is a dynamic civilization with the Jewish
religion as its core. Kaplan is the author of many philosophical works
on Judaism: *Judaism as a Civilization* (1934), *Judaism in Transition*
(1936), and *The Future of the American Jew* (1948), among others.

[41]

KAUFMANN KOHLER (1843-1926)

Born Fürth, Germany; died New York City. Rabbi, educator, and theologian.
PLAQUE: *Cast bronze, 5⅛″ x 3⅞″, by Mantel. FB 600.*

Kaufmann Kohler studied under Samson Raphael Hirsch in Frankfurt-am-Main and, although diametrically opposed to Hirsch's views, he later said that no individual had so great an influence upon him. Kohler emigrated to the United States in 1869 firmly convinced of the efficacy of the scientific method for Jewish research and scholarship and of the necessity of harmonizing Judaism with modern thought and life. He served as rabbi in Detroit (1869-71), Chicago (1871-79), and New York City (1879-1903). In 1903 he became president of the Hebrew Union College. A radical critic, constructive theologian, and man of profound belief, Kohler was the most powerful intellect in early American Reform Judaism. The Declaration of Principles drafted at the Pittsburgh Conference (1885), and which served as Reform Judaism's statement of beliefs for the following half-century, was for the most part his. Kohler was a prolific writer, and his *Jewish Theology* (1910) remains today one of the most lucid and literate books ever written on this subject.

LUCIEN LÉVY-BRUHL (1857-1939)

Born and died Paris, France. Sociologist and philosopher.
PLAQUE: *Cast bronze, 4¼″ x 3¾″, by I. Sors. FB 685.*

As a follower of Auguste Comte's positivism, Lucien Lévy-Brühl represented a philosophy of social realism. His goal was the establishment of social and moral laws that would resemble natural laws. As a result, he felt that sociology should dedicate itself to the rediscovery of the various developmental stages in the history of man. Many of his most important books concerned themselves with the qualities and characteristics of primitive societies: *How Natives Think* (1910), *The Primitive Mentality* (1922), and *Primitives and the Supernatural* (1931), among others. The foremost French social philosopher after the death of Durkheim, Lévy-Brühl was professor of philosophy at the Sorbonne (1899-1927), a member of the Académie des Sciences Morales et Politiques and of the Institut Français, and editor of the *Revue philosophique de la France et de l'étranger.*

SAMUEL DAVID LUZZATTO (1800-1865)

Born Trieste, Italy; died Padua, Italy. Philologist, poet, and Biblical exegete.
PLAQUE: *Cast bronze, 5¼″ x 4″, by I. Sors. FB 568.*

Samuel David Luzzatto (ShaDaL) was recognized for his poetry and philological treatises while still a young man. At the age of twenty-one he was commissioned to translate the prayerbook into Italian and eight years later was appointed to the faculty of the newly established Padua Rabbinical College. He was the first scholar to devote himself to the study of Syriac or to attempt the compilation of an Aramaic grammar, and the first Jew to amend the Biblical text. Luzzatto nonetheless believed that Judaism could survive only if the laws were strictly obeyed; he stood firmly opposed to philosophical Judaism. He argued that the critical faculties must be used to find proofs for religion, not to fabricate a rational basis for it. Judaism's ethic is purely emotional, he claimed, and has no basis in rationalism. Author of an Italian translation of the Pentateuch and Haftoroth, Luzzatto also brought Jewish poetry of the Spanish Golden Age into the academic limelight with his publication of Judah Halevi's *Diwan* (1864).

JUDAH LEON MAGNES (1877-1948)

Born San Francisco, California; died New York City. Rabbi and educator.
PLAQUE: *Cast bronze, diam. 4⅝", by Kormis. FB 1022.*

Judah Leon Magnes was ordained a rabbi by the Hebrew Union College in 1900 and two years later received his Ph.D. from the University of Heidelberg. While serving as a congregational rabbi in New York City (1904-11), Magnes was secretary of the Federation of American Zionists (1905-08) and chairman of the Executive Committee of the Kehillah (a short-lived [1909-22] union of Jewish communal organizations in New York City), establishing its important Bureau of Jewish Education in 1910. He helped to found the Yiddish daily *Der Tag*, the Society for the Advancement of Judaism (1912), and, during World War I, the Joint Distribution Committee. A founder of the Hebrew University, Magnes raised funds for its establishment and drew up the basic plans for its educational program. He served as the University's first chancellor (1925-35) and as its president (1935-48). A noted pacifist, Magnes was an outspoken advocate of bi-nationality for Israel based on Arab-Jewish cooperation.

SOLOMON ben JOSHUA MAIMON (1754-1800)

Born Nieszwicz, Lithuania; died Nieder-Siegersdorf, Germany. Philosopher.
PLAQUE: *Cast bronze, 4⅜" x 3¾", by I. Sors. FB 691.*

Solomon Maimon was considered a heretic for his attempts to make cabalism into a philosophy. Consequently he abandoned his studies for the rabbinate and went to Berlin with the intention of pursuing medicine. Adopted as a disciple by Moses Mendelssohn, who immediately recognized the young man's potential, Maimon nonetheless spent ten years in the pursuit of pleasure in Berlin and Hamburg. Not until 1790 did he begin the work that soon after brought him fame. Moved by the newly popular Kantian philosophy, he wrote a brilliant critical study that led Kant himself to say that, of all his critics, Maimon alone truly understood his philosophy. Maimon insisted that, since knowledge of *things* must necessarily be subjective, philosophy must limit itself to pure thought, logic, and mathematics. His work had great influence and became the basis of all future Kant criticism.

MAIMONIDES (Rabbi Moses ben Maimon) (1135-1204)

Born Córdova, Spain; died Cairo, Egypt. Philosopher.
PLAQUE: *Cast bronze, 6¼″ x 4¾″, by I. Sors. FB 780.*

Maimonides fled Spain in 1148 when the Almohades captured his native city. After years of wandering he settled in Cairo and began the work that established his reputation as one of the greatest scholars and philosophers in Jewish history. He was the author both of a commentary on the Mishnah and of the *Mishnah Torah*, a scientific categorization of all Talmudic material that a layman, jurist, or theologian might require. It was one of the most prodigious works ever accomplished and included all traditional explanations, statutes, and regulations. But it is for his *Moreh Nebuchim* that he is best remembered. This book was an attempt to harmonize the Bible and rabbinic literature with philosophy (especially with Aristotle). It discussed the divine attributes, proofs of God's existence, the requisites of prophecy, and the origin of evil and also contained a brilliant refutation of Aristotle's "eternity of matter." A work of vast profundity, the *Moreh Nebuchim* has influenced Judaeo-Christian thought since the time of its publication.

ALEXANDER MARX (1878-1953)

Born Elberfeld, Germany; died New York City. Historian and educator.
PLAQUE: *Cast bronze, 6³⁄₁₆″ x 5¼″, by I. Sors. FB 602.*

Alexander Marx studied for a time at the rabbinical seminary in Berlin and received his Ph.D. from the University of Königsberg in 1903. In that same year he came to the United States, where he assumed the post of professor of history and director of libraries at The Jewish Theological Seminary of America (1903-53). Marx was a superb scholar and a prolific writer of books and articles. His best known work is *A History of the Jewish People* (1927), which he wrote in collaboration with Max Margolis. Among his many other books are *Seder Olam* (1903), *Aims and Tasks of Jewish Historiography* (1918), and *Moses Maimonides* (1935). The recipient of several honorary degrees, Marx served as vice-president of the American Jewish Historical Society.

MENASSEH ben ISRAEL (1604-1657)

Born Lisbon(?), Portugal; died Middleburg, Holland. Rabbi and author.
PLAQUE: *Cast bronze, 5⅛″ x 4⁵⁄₁₆″, by Kormis. FB 601.*

Menasseh ben Israel, a Marrano by birth, was taken to Amsterdam as a child and when only eighteen was appointed rabbi of the Neveh Shalom congregation. He was a prolific writer with a wide contemporary audience, and among his many works was *El Conciliador* (1632), an attempt to reconcile contradictory passages in scripture. His greatest fame, however, stems from the highly successful *Hope of Israel*, a volume he wrote in 1650 that soon gained the attention of Oliver Cromwell. Largely through ben Israel's efforts Cromwell was persuaded to convene a conference at Whitehall in 1655 on the issue of Jewish resettlement in England. The conference of statesmen, lawyers, and theologians determined that there was nothing in English law to prevent Jews from living in that country. As a result Jewish settlers in England were encouraged to establish homes there openly for the first time in more than three hundred and fifty years.

MOSES MENDELSSOHN (1729-1786)

Born Dessau, Germany; died Berlin, Germany. Philosopher.
MEDAL : *Struck silver, diam. 1¹⁵⁄₁₆″, by I. Abraham. FB 28.*

Moses Mendelssohn followed his teacher to Berlin in 1743 and soon became a very successful tutor in his own right. In 1754 he met the great dramatist Gotthold Lessing, who published Mendelssohn's *Philosophical Conversations* the following year. He was launched to fame with this condemnation of German neglect of native philosophers and upon the publication of *Phaedon* in 1767 became known as the "German Socrates." In 1783, after many years of working toward the emancipation of the Jews, Mendelssohn published his epochal translation of the Pentateuch, a work that not only led the Jews to a knowledge of the German language, but also to a subsequent desire for integration. *Jerusalem* (1783) was a brilliant, pragmatic plea for tolerance. In this highly original work Mendelssohn contended that if two nations need two different forms of government, then there is no reason why two individuals cannot need two different religions. In a strictly modern vein, Mendelssohn echoed the ancient prophets in his assertion that ethical conduct is the only true test of a religion's validity.

HENRY PEREIRA MENDES (1852-1937)

Born Birmingham, England; died Mt. Vernon, New York. Rabbi and educator.
PLAQUE: *Cast bronze, 5¼″ x 4¹⁵⁄₁₆″, by Mantel. FB 693.*

Henry Pereira Mendes was educated at Northwick and University Colleges in London, served as rabbi in Manchester for two years, and in 1877 accepted a call from Congregation Shearith Israel in New York. During his forty-three years as rabbi of that historic synagogue, Mendes helped to establish Montefiore Hospital, the Crippled Children's East Side Free School, Horeb School for Jewish Deaf-Mutes, and New York Kehillah. He was co-founder with Sabato Morais of The Jewish Theological Seminary of America and was president of that institution from 1897 to 1902. He also organized the Union of Orthodox Jewish Congregations of America (1898) and was its president (1898-1913). Among the many causes for which he crusaded were liberal immigration laws and total nonsectarianism in public schools. A prolific writer, Mendes was known for his poems, hymns, and Jewish religious and educational books.

SABATO MORAIS (1823-1897)

Born Leghorn, Italy; died Philadelphia, Pennsylvania. Rabbi and educator.
PLAQUE: *Cast bronze, diam. 5¾″, by I. Sors. FB 742.*

Educated in Italy, Sabato Morais went to London in 1846 as a Hebrew teacher in an orphan asylum. Five years later he was called to the leadership of Mikveh Israel Congregation in Philadelphia. In 1867 he helped to found Maimonides College, the first Jewish college in the United States, and was professor of the Bible during that institution's seven-year existence. In 1881 he established a fund for the settlement of Russian immigrants in agricultural colonies in New Jersey and assisted in the management of those colonies for many years. In response to Reform Judaism's Pittsburgh Platform, he worked with Henry Pereira Mendes in the founding of The Jewish Theological Seminary of America (1886) and served as its president and as professor of the Bible until his death.

ABRAHAM A. NEUMAN (1890-   )

Born Brezan, Austria. Rabbi, historian, and educator.
PLAQUE: *Cast bronze, 7¾″ x 6⁵⁄₁₆″, by Mantel. FB 540.*

Abraham Neuman was brought to the United States at the age of eight. After graduation from Columbia University in 1909, he was ordained a rabbi by The Jewish Theological Seminary of America (1912). He joined the faculty of Dropsie College the following year, was made a full professor in 1934, and became its president in 1941. He has served as rabbi of Philadelphia's B'nai Jeshurun Congregation (1919-27) and Mikveh Israel Synagogue (1927-43, honorary since 1943). Noted as a lecturer, biographer, and historian, Neuman was one of the first to make extensive use of rabbinic responsa in the study of history. He has also co-edited the *Jewish Quarterly Review*, been vice-president of the American Jewish Historical Society, and served as revising editor of the *Universal Jewish Encyclopedia*.

SOLOMON REINACH (1858-1932)

Born Saint-Germain-en-Laye, France; died Paris, France. Archaeologist and historian.
PLAQUE: *Cast bronze, 5⁹⁄₁₆″ x 4″, by I. Sors. FB 796.*

Solomon Reinach's first work (which appeared while he was still a student) was the initial French translation of a Schopenhauer treatise. Reinach, a first-rate archaeologist, directed excavations at Delos, Lesbos, and Carthage. He later became curator of the National Museum of France. His *Apollo*, a general history of the arts, was published in ninety-six French editions and translated into many foreign languages. An agnostic, Reinach was profoundly interested in religion from an historical and sociological point of view. He considered Judaism to be a part of the general ethical and social development of man. In this light he pursued studies to discover in what ways it was similar to other religions. Reinach was the author of more than seventy volumes on archaeology, art, philosophy, sociology, and history. Among his finest works is *Cults, Myths, and Religions* (five volumes, 1905-23).

ABRAHAM SIMON WOLF ROSENBACH (1876-1952)

PLAQUE: *Cast bronze, 5⅛″ x 3¹³⁄₁₆″, by I. Sors. FB 781.*
Born and died Philadelphia, Pennsylvania. Writer and bibliographer.

Abraham Rosenbach was still a young man when he became secretary of the family book business, the field in which his people had been engaged since 1785. Within a short time he was a familiar and respected figure at auctions throughout the world, where his astronomical bids soon established a new level of value on literary rarities. During his lifetime he purchased a record total of seventy-two collections of rare books and manuscripts. Rosenbach was president of the American Jewish Historical Society, of Gratz College, and of the American Friends of the Hebrew University. He was a Ph.D. from the University of Pennsylvania (1901) and the author of *The Unpublishable Memoirs* (1917), *An American Jewish Bibliography* (1926), and *The Libraries of the Presidents of the United States* (1934).

CECIL ROTH (1899-   )

Born London, England. Historian.
PLAQUE: *Cast bronze, diam. 5″, by Kormis. FB 865.*

Cecil Roth was graduated from Oxford University in 1924, and since that time he has become one of the world's foremost Jewish historians. Notable among his many works are his biographies of the Rothschilds, the Sassoons, Joseph Nasi, and Menasseh ben Israel, as well as his *Short History of the Jewish People* (1936) and *The Jewish Contribution to Civilization* (1938). He has contributed particularly to scholarship in the fields of Jewish art and Jewish history in England and Italy during the Medieval and Baroque periods. Roth, president of the Jewish Historical Society of England from 1936 to 1945 and again in 1955-56, has also been editor-in-chief of the *Standard Jewish Encyclopedia* and a contributor to *Encyclopaedia Brittanica*, *Encyclopaedia Judaica*, and *Cambridge Medieval History*. Since 1939 he has been a reader in Jewish studies at the University of Oxford.

SOLOMON SCHECHTER (1850-1915)

Born Fokshan, Romania; died New York City. Hebraist and educator.
PLAQUE: *Cast bronze, diam. 5⅛", by Mantel. FB 424.*

Solomon Schechter received a rabbinical diploma in 1879. Three
years later he settled in England, where he served as reader in
Talmud and rabbinic literature at the University of Cambridge
(1890-1901). In 1896 he astounded scholars by his identification of
a fragmentary manuscript as being part of the oldest book of the
Apocrypha—*The Wisdom of Ben Sira,* or *Ecclesiasticus.* Immediately
thereafter he went to Cairo to investigate the Genizah (a repository
for old or damaged books) and returned to Cambridge with 50,000
manuscripts and fragments. Schechter believed that Judaism could
sustain diversity of opinion without sacrificing tradition. As president
of The Jewish Theological Seminary of America (1901-15), his aim
was to create in American Jewry a sense of kinship with Judaism of
other ages and other lands. Schechter was an editor of the *Jewish
Encyclopedia,* the *Jewish Quarterly Review,* and the first Jewish Publication Society translation of the Bible. Among his many books are
Some Aspects of Rabbinic Theology (1909), *Documents of Jewish
Sectaries* (1910), and essays collected in *Studies in Judaism* (three
volumes, 1898, 1908, 1924).

GERSHOM MENDEZ SEIXAS (1745-1816)

Born and died New York City. Rabbi.
PLAQUE: *Cast bronze, 5¹¹⁄₁₆″ x 4¾″, by I. Sors. FB 694.*

As Rabbi of Congregation Shearith Israel in New York City (1766-1816), Gershom Mendez Seixas refused to serve in British-held territory during the American Revolution. Fleeing with the Torahs and other sancta of his synagogue, he went first to Stratford, Connecticut, and then to Philadelphia, where he helped to found Congregation Mikveh Israel (1780). In 1783 he successfully sought revisions in a constitutional clause newly adopted by the Pennsylvania legislature requiring a religious examination for office seekers. Seixas returned to New York in 1784 and was one of fourteen clergymen participating in George Washington's first inaugural (1787). He was a trustee of Columbia College (1787-1815) and founder of the Hebra Hased Ve Amet (1802), a society for the relief of the sick and the burial of the dead. An ardent patriot, Seixas was one of the most vigorous defenders of the American cause during the Revolution and of the much-maligned Madison Administration during the War of 1812.

ABBA HILLEL SILVER (1893-   )

Born Neinstadt, Lithuania. Rabbi.
PLAQUE: *Cast bronze, diam. 4⅜″, by Kormis. FB 908.*

Abba Hillel Silver, ordained by the Hebrew Union College in 1915, is one of the most influential clergymen of the twentieth century. As rabbi of The Temple in Cleveland, Ohio, since 1917, he has been very active in civic affairs and has served as chairman of the Cleveland Jewish Welfare Fund. In 1943 Silver was asked by Chaim Weizmann to assume the political leadership of Zionism in America. Heeding the call, Silver was president and honorary president of the Zionist Organization of America. As chairman of the American section of the Jewish Agency, he was one of the most eloquent speakers to appear before the United Nations in favor of a Jewish state. He is a noted orator and has served as university preacher at Harvard, Cornell, Chicago, Syracuse, and Purdue Universities. Among Silver's many works are *Messianic Speculations in Israel* (1927), *Religion in a Changing World* (1930), and *Where Judaism Differed* (1956).

BARUCH SPINOZA (1632-1677)

Born Amsterdam, Holland; died The Hague, Holland. Philosopher.
MEDAL: *Cast bronze, diam. 2¹¹⁄₁₆″, by P. Turin. FB 27.*

Baruch Spinoza, a lens grinder by trade, was excommunicated for blasphemy from the Jewish community in 1656. Although he is known today as the father of modern metaphysics and of moral and political philosophy, he was recognized only as a heretic during his lifetime (save by the University of Heidelberg, which offered him a professorship in 1674). Spinoza was a monist. He believed that all existence is based in God, that all seemingly separate things are but aspects of the divinity, and that man must attempt to understand the workings of the universe, accept his place in the world, and participate happily in God's immutable plan. Spinoza was also an outspoken defender of freedom of opinion and of the democratic form of government. His *Treatise on Religious and Political Philosophy* (1670) and *Ethics* (1677) have had an inestimable influence on modern philosophers.

ISAAC MAYER WISE (1819-1900)

Born Steingrub, Bohemia; died Cincinnati, Ohio. Rabbi and educator.
PLAQUE: *Cast bronze, 6½" x 4⁵⁄₁₆", by B. Schatz. FB 158.*

Isaac Mayer Wise emigrated to America in 1846 and, after serving as rabbi in Albany, accepted a position with Cincinnati's Temple Bene Jeshurun (1854-1900). Wise founded and edited two weekly newspapers, *The American Israelite* (English) and *Die Deborah* (German), and was the author of an American Reform prayerbook. He also wrote several novels and books on Jewish history and theology, and an autobiography entitled *Reminiscences.* He organized the Union of American Hebrew Congregations (1873), and founded the Hebrew Union College (1875) and the Central Conference of American Rabbis (1889). Through these organizations Wise looked forward to the development of a Judaism that would be American both in character and in outlook. A great educator, liberal, and idealist, Wise is known as the founder of American Reform Judaism.

STEPHEN SAMUEL WISE (1874-1949)

Born Budapest, Hungary; died New York City. Rabbi.
PLAQUE: *Cast bronze, 6⅜" x 4⅞", by I. Sors. FB 614.*

Stephen Wise was brought to America as an infant. Following his graduation from Columbia University in 1892, he began a long and distinguished career in the rabbinate. He spent six years as rabbi in Portland, Oregon, and upon returning to New York City established the Free Synagogue, which he guided from 1907 until his death. As a noted orator, Wise was an outspoken advocate of social and political reform. No just cause lacked his eager support; no unjust cause escaped his wrath. He founded the American Jewish Congress, represented that organization at the Versailles Peace Conference (1919), and served as its president for seven consecutive terms. In 1922 Wise founded the Jewish Institute of Religion as a rabbinical seminary. Stephen Wise, a dedicated Zionist, served as president of the Zionist Organization of America from 1936 to 1938 and of the World Jewish Congress from 1936 until his death.

LUDWIG LAZAR ZAMENHOF (1859-1917)

Born Bialystok, Poland; died Warsaw, Poland. Linguist.
PLAQUE: *Cast bronze, diam. 5⅝", by A. Gubowizc. FB 8.*

Ludwig Zamenhof devoted his entire life to but one thing: worldwide acceptance of the language that he had developed, Esperanto. Motivated by a highly developed universalist attitude, he felt that universal brotherhood was most impeded by the world's many different languages and man's resultant inability to communicate with his fellow man. Zamenhof published his first Esperanto textbook, *Dro Esperanto (The Hopeful One)* in 1887. The language is based on a mere 900 root words (as contrasted with the 20,000 in the typical modern language) and possesses but sixteen grammatical rules. In 1905 Zamenhof called the first international congress of Esperanto, at which students from nearly every country were in attendance. His disciples have regularly increased, and today there are over two million people speaking his universal language.

Public Affairs

GREAT JEWISH PORTRAITS IN METAL

LUDWIG BAMBERGER (1823-1899)

Born Mainz, Germany; died Berlin, Germany. Economist.
PLAQUE: *Cast bronze, 5" x 4", by I. Sors. FB 623.*

Ludwig Bamberger was educated in the law at the Universities of Giessen, Heidelberg, and Göttingen. Condemned to death for his activities in the insurrections of 1848, he fled the country and settled in Paris, where he became a banker. He remained there until 1868 when, pardon having been granted to all political offenders, he returned to Mainz. He was elected to Parliament and, following the Franco-Prussian War, was invited by Bismarck to the Versailles Peace Conference, where he helped to establish the indemnity owed by France. As a member of the Diet (1869-93) he championed free trade and vigorously defended the maintenance of the gold standard. As the years passed, Bamberger grew more and more disenchanted with Bismarck, particularly with his colonial policy. He defended his opposition to the Chancellor in his book *Bismarck Posthumous* (1899).

DAVID BEN-GURION (1886-   )

Born Plonsk, Poland. Statesman.
PLAQUE: *Cast bronze, diam. 4⅝", by Kormis. FB 907.*

In 1903 David Ben-Gurion helped to found the Zionist Socialist Society and three years later went to Palestine as a laborer. He organized a Jewish self-defense movement in Galilee, but was temporarily thwarted in his efforts to unite the Jews when, during World War I, he was expelled by the Turks. Undaunted, however, Ben-Gurion journeyed to the United States and assisted in the crystallization of Jewish Zionist opinion in this country. In 1921 he returned to Palestine, where he became General Secretary of the Histadrut (General Federation of Labor). Ben-Gurion was elected to the executive body of the World Zionist Organization in 1933 and from that time forward played an important role in the establishment of the Jewish State. He was Prime Minister and Minister of Defense during Israel's formative years and, after retiring at the age of sixty-seven, resumed leadership in 1955. Ben-Gurion, a scholar as well as a statesman, can in large part be credited with the phenomenal domestic and foreign success that Israel has witnessed since her founding in 1948.

JUDAH P. BENJAMIN (1811-1884)

Born St. Thomas, West Indies; died Paris, France. Lawyer, statesman, and politician.
PLAQUE: *Cast bronze, 3⅞" x 2¾", by I. Sors. FB 626.*

A masterful orator with an exemplary knowledge of the law, Judah P. Benjamin attended Yale University (1825-27), became an attorney in New Orleans, and soon was known for accepting and winning "impossible" cases. He was counsel for a number of railroads and, in one instance, for the United States Government. As a member of the

Louisiana state legislature (1842-52) Benjamin secured the establishment of a state university and the abolition of the penalty of imprisonment for debtors. In 1852 Benjamin was elected to the United States Senate, where he was the most articulate defender of the South's position during the turbulent period before the Civil War. When Louisiana seceded from the Union he became Attorney General of the Confederacy, then Secretary of War, and, after 1862, Secretary of State. Known as the "brains of the Confederacy," he served as President Jefferson Davis's right-hand man. Benjamin fled to England after Appomattox and became one of that country's foremost barristers, being appointed queen's counsel in 1872.

ITZHAK BEN-ZVI (1884-1963)

Born Poltava, Russia. Statesman and author.
PLAQUE: *Cast bronze, 5" x 4½₆", by Kormis. FB 902.*

Influenced by Zionism in his youth, Itzhak Ben-Zvi went to Palestine for the first time in 1903. He returned to his native land, however, and helped to organize the Poale Zion (Workers for Zion). Soon exiled to Siberia for his activities in defense of his fellow Jews during the pogroms, he escaped and spent two years in Germany and Switzerland. In 1907 Ben-Zvi settled in Palestine, where he entered into local politics and, following World War I, helped to establish the Histadrut and the Knesset. He was elected to the presidium of the Va'ad Le'umi (Jewish National Council) in 1920 and was made its chairman in 1931 and president in 1944. Ben-Zvi was a member of the first Knesset and was the President of Israel after assuming that post upon the death of Chaim Weizmann in 1952. He was also a distinguished ethnologist and was the author of such works as *Arabs and Moslems* (1926), *The Moslem World and the Arab World* (1937), *The Exiled and the Redeemed* (1953), and *Four Hundred Years of Turkish Rule in Palestine* (1955).

LÉON BLUM (1872-1950)

Born Paris, France; died near Versailles, France. Statesman and politician.
PLAQUE: *Cast bronze, 3½" x 2¼", by Reynauld. FB 150.*

Léon Blum first involved himself in the socialist movement during the Dreyfus Affair. By 1919 he had been elected deputy and was thereafter the acknowledged head of the French Socialist Party. In 1936 he became the first Jewish Premier of France. Within a brief period his Administration secured laws providing for a forty-hour work week, collective bargaining and compulsory arbitration, and the nationalization of the Bank of France. He resigned in the face of conservative opposition to his economic policies but was Vice-Premier in 1937-38 and Premier again in 1938. A defendant in the abortive war guilt trial held in 1942 at Riom, he was later surrendered to the Germans by Marshal Pétain and interned in a concentration camp. He was liberated in 1945 and the following year headed a one-month interim government.

BENJAMIN DISRAELI, Earl of Beaconsfield (1804-1881)

Born and died London, England. Statesman and novelist.
MEDAL: *Struck aluminum, diam. 1¾", by O. Birm. FB 152.*

After an apprenticeship in a solicitors' firm, failure in the publishing business, and extensive traveling, Benjamin Disraeli achieved overnight fame with the publication of his novel *Vivian Grey* (1826). This was immediately followed by a number of literary triumphs. The future Earl of Beaconsfield turned to politics, however, and was defeated in four successive attempts at election to Parliament. He was finally elected in 1837 and quickly became known in the House of Commons for his brilliant wit, his command of facts, and his unwavering independence. In 1846, upon the fall of Sir Robert Peel, Disraeli became a leader of the Conservative Party. He usually served as able and eloquent spokesman for the opposition but did hold the office of Chancellor of the Exchequer (1852, 1858) and Prime Minister (1868, 1874-80). He was greatly respected by Queen Victoria and in 1876 was named Earl of Beaconsfield. Through intellect, resourcefulness, and courage he rose to the leadership of the party of the aristocracy. Disraeli, who was baptized as a child, was uncommonly proud of his Jewish background.

ALFRED DREYFUS (1859-1935)

Born Mulhouse, France; died Paris, France. Army officer.
PLAQUE: *Cast bronze, 5¾" x 3¹⁵⁄₁₆", by I. Sors. FB 653.*

Captain Alfred Dreyfus was the only Jewish officer on the French General Staff when in 1894 he was accused of passing information to the Germans. The Army, fearful of public censure, suppressed evidence in his favor, and Dreyfus was convicted of treason on the basis of forged documents. He was sent to the penal colony on Devil's Island, while the real traitor, Count Esterhazy, was tried and acquitted. Dreyfus was brought to trial again, reconvicted, and it was not until 1899 that he was pardoned by the President of France. The Supreme Court of Appeals cleared his name of all guilt in 1906, and he was reinstated in the Army with the rank of major. The Dreyfus Affair was one of the most serious and highly publicized scandals of all time and was a major factor in the rise both of Zionism and of socialism in Europe.

ABBA S. EBAN (1915-   )

Born Capetown, South Africa. Diplomat.
PLAQUE: *Cast bronze, diam. 5⅜", by Wein. FB 1101.*

Abba Eban was educated at the University of Cambridge, where in 1938 he became lecturer in Arabic, Persian, and Hebrew literature. During World War II he served as liaison between Allied Headquarters and the Jewish population of Palestine. At the age of thirty-three Eban argued his country's cause in the United Nations and as Israel's representative in that world assembly (1948-59) proved himself to be a most eloquent debater. Particularly notable was his brilliant defense of his country's occupation of the Sinai Peninsula in 1956. Eban also served as Ambassador to the United States (1948-59) and, since his return to Israel in 1959, has been Minister of Education and Culture. He is the author of numerous articles, and his speeches were published in 1957 as *Voice of Israel—Selected Speeches of Abba Eban.*

ISAAC FRANKS (1759-1822)

Born New York City; died Philadelphia, Pennsylvania. Army officer.
PLAQUE: *Cast bronze, 4¹⁵⁄₁₆" x 4¹⁄₁₆", by I. Sors. FB 583.*

At the age of seventeen Isaac Franks joined the American revolutionists as a volunteer. He served under General George Washington at the Battle of Long Island and was later held prisoner by the British for three months. He escaped, however, and served as forage-master at West Point from 1877 until 1881. In the latter year he received a Congressional appointment as ensign in the Seventh Massachusetts Regiment, but he was soon forced to resign due to ill health. In 1789 Franks was appointed a notary public—an office of some distinction in the late eighteenth century—and five years later was made lieutenant-colonel in the Second Regiment, Philadelphia County. He was a justice of the peace after 1795. Colonel Franks was one of America's less known but greatest patriots and public servants.

SAMUEL GOMPERS (1850-1924)

Born London, England; died San Antonio, Texas. Labor leader.
PLAQUE: *Cast zinc, 5⅛" x 5", by A. Eisenberg. FB 242.*

Samuel Gompers emigrated to the United States in 1863. While still a young man he became active in the Cigarmakers Union, which, under his leadership, became the model for all future unions. In 1886 Gompers founded the American Federation of Labor (now the AFL-CIO), serving as its president (with the exception of one year) until his death. Demanding one union for each trade in all of North America, Gompers asked only for better wages, better working hours, and better living conditions. He felt that there was a distinct line between capital and labor and that unions should never go into business for themselves. Rather was it their duty to work for better conditions within the status quo. Among his publications were *Labor in Europe and America* (1910), *American Labor and the War* (1919), and *Seventy Years of Life and Labor* (two volumes, 1920), which remains unsurpassed as a chronicle of the growth of unionism in America.

REBECCA GRATZ (1781-1869)

Born and died Philadelphia, Pennsylvania. Educator and philanthropist.
PLAQUE: *Cast bronze, 5⅛" x 3⅞", by Mantel. FB 96.*

Rebecca Gratz devoted her life to religious, educational, and charitable causes. She organized fuel and sewing societies and, early aware of the need for an institution for orphans, helped to found the Philadelphia Orphan Asylum in 1815, acting as secretary of its board of managers for forty years. It is especially as a pioneer in the field of Jewish philanthropy that she is remembered. The Female Hebrew Benevolent Society was founded by Miss Gratz in 1819, followed in 1838 by the first Jewish Sunday school in the United States, where she served as the school's superintendent until her death. After years of untiring effort she also succeeded in establishing a Jewish Foster Home. Described to Sir Walter Scott by her friend Washington Irving, her kindness and good works inspired the great Scottish novelist to use her as the model for Rebecca, the heroine of *Ivanhoe*.

ERNEST GRUENING (1887-   )

Born New York City. Journalist, politician, and government official.
PLAQUE: *Cast bronze, 5" x 3⅝", by I. Sors. FB 816.*

A graduate of Harvard University (A.B., 1907; M.D., 1912), Ernest Gruening served as an editor of various newspapers throughout the country until 1920, when he became managing editor of *The Nation*. In Maine he founded the *Portland Evening News* in 1927 and was editor of that journal until he joined the Department of Interior as director of its Division of Territories and Island Possessions (1934-39). Gruening was Governor of Alaska from 1939 to 1953 and, as keynoter at the state constitutional convention in 1955, became one of Alaska's first two Senators when she joined the Union the following year. He has held that office ever since. Gruening is the author of *Mexico and Its Heritage* (1928), *The Public Pays* (1931), and *The State of Alaska* (1954).

[58]

MAXIMILIAN HARDEN (1861-1927)

Born and died Berlin, Germany. Journalist.
PLAQUE: *Cast bronze, 5⅛″ x 3¹¹⁄₁₆″, by I. Sors. FB 671.*

Maximilian Harden (né Felix Witkowski) was an ardent admirer of Bismarck and founded his newspaper, *Die Zukunft* (1893), in support of that great German leader. Well-versed in literature, Harden wrote superb, though outspoken, essays and editorials on contemporary political and cultural topics. His brilliant career seemed ended, however, in 1902, when he was named defendant in a libel suit brought by one of Kaiser Wilhelm's protégés. He was vindicated when Prince Eulenburg, whose intrigues he had exposed, fled the country. During the First World War Harden was a leading critic of the German High Command and, in the postwar period, of the Weimar Republic. Although a convert to Christianity, he maintained an interest in Jewish affairs throughout his life and manifested a real concern for the success of Zionism. Harden was a great journalist and a man of uncompromising principles; not even an attempt on his life could silence him or subdue his independence.

THEODOR HERZL (1860-1904)

Born Budapest, Hungary; died Vienna, Austria. Journalist and founder of political Zionism.
PLAQUE: *Cast bronze, 2⅜″ x 2¹⁄₁₆″, by Kormis. FB 156.*

Theodor Herzl was exposed to the virulent antisemitism of the Dreyfus Affair while serving as Paris correspondent for a Viennese newspaper. He became convinced of the need for Zion and in 1896 wrote *The Jewish State*, in which he argued that the Jews were a people possessing all of the human and material resources needed for a political union. Their assimilation into Western civilization was impossible, he contended, because over the centuries their persecutors had made of them a people separate from the rest of mankind. Herzl was nonetheless unable to win the necessary Jewish financiers to his cause and, in 1897, in order to mobilize popular aid, he convened the first Zionist congress. He also contacted world political leaders in an effort to negotiate for support and land. Gradually the needed support arose, both from his fellow Jews and from various heads of state. But shortly before his death the sixth Zionist congress, demanding Palestine or nothing, refused Great Britain's offer of a part of East Africa. In 1948 Herzl's dream was fulfilled, and, in accordance with his wishes, his ashes were buried in Jerusalem.

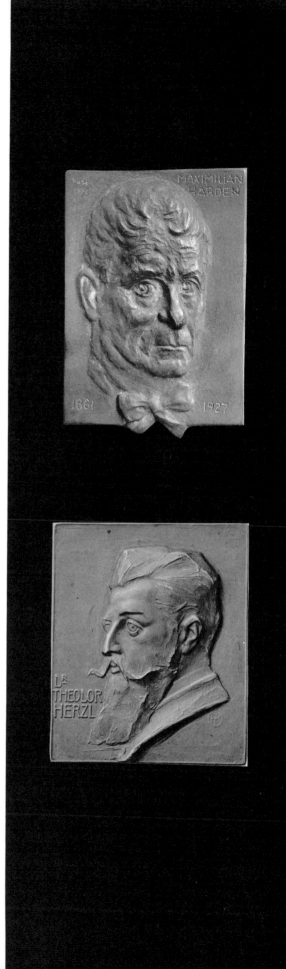

SIDNEY HILLMAN (1887-1946)

Born Zagare, Lithuania; died Point Lookout, L. I., New York. Labor leader.
PLAQUE: *Cast bronze, diam. 4¹³⁄₁₆″, by A. Eisenberg. FB 772.*

Having served ten months in prison for underground activities during the 1905 Revolution, Sidney Hillman left Russia at the age of twenty. After a short stay in England, he came to America and began work with a large Chicago clothing manufacturer. During a bitter strike in 1910, he helped to settle the dispute with his Impartial Arbitration Plan, the model for many such future plans. Shortly thereafter he became the first president of the Amalgamated Clothing Workers Union (1915-46). Moderate in his views, he believed that the interests of labor are best served by cooperation and the resultant well-being of industry. President Franklin D. Roosevelt appointed Hillman to the Labor Advisory Board of the National Recovery Act and to the chairmanship of the Labor Division of the War Production Board. Known as a "labor statesman," he was a founder and vice president of the Congress of Industrial Organizations (now the AFL-CIO).

LESLIE HORE-BELISHA, 1st Baron of Devonport (1893-1957)

Born Kilburn, England; died Reims, France. Politician and government official.
PLAQUE: *Cast bronze, diam. 4¼″, by Kormis. FB 409.*

Leslie Hore-Belisha was educated at Oxford, Heidelberg, and the Sorbonne. He attained the rank of major during the First World War and, after a brief career in the law, was elected to Parliament in 1923. As Minister of Transport (1934-37) he instituted the revolutionary and highly successful system of traffic guides known as "Belisha Beacons." From 1937 to 1940 Hore-Belisha was Secretary of State for War. During those three years he entirely revamped the Army, making it possible for privates to attain officer's rank, increasing mechanization, instituting pay raises, and expanding the Territorial Army. By 1940 it was no longer an army of the élite, but rather a truly national army not unprepared for World War II. Hore-Belisha was knighted by Queen Elizabeth II in 1954.

VLADIMIR JABOTINSKY (1880-1940)

Born Odessa, Russia; died Camp Betar, near Hunter, N. Y. Zionist leader.
PLAQUE: *Cast bronze, 6³⁄₁₆″ x 4⅜″, by I. Sors. FB 564.*

A man of action who demanded action of others, Vladimir Jabotinksy was an early advocate of Jewish self-defense units against pogroms and a voice in the struggle for minority rights. He demanded that Jewish regiments fight on the Palestine front during World War I, vainly hoping that this would be a means of wresting Zion from the Turks. He later organized the first self-defense unit in Jerusalem and in 1921 joined the Zionist Executive. In opposition to Chaim Weizmann's leniency toward British policy, Jabotinsky called for immediate mass immigration. He felt that world Jewry was being betrayed by its leaders and resigned from the Executive to form an organization in opposition to official Zionism. He urged the evacuation of Eastern European Jews to Palestine and, when the Second World War began, again demanded a Jewish army. He remains perhaps the most controversial figure in the entire history of Zionism.

HAROLD JOSEPH LASKI (1893-1950)

Born Manchester, England; died London, England. Political scientist.
PLAQUE: *Cast bronze, diam. 4¾", by Kormis. FB 526.*

Harold Laski was educated in England, taught at McGill (1914-16) and Harvard (1916-20) Universities, and in 1926 became University of London professor of political science at the School of Economics and Political Science. Possibly Great Britain's greatest exponent of socialism, he served on the executive committees of the Fabian Society (1922-36) and of the Labour Party (1936-49). It was in *A Grammar of Politics* (1925) that he first expounded his radical ideas —even saying that the state exists solely in order to protect the individual and that the individual has the right not only to criticize but also to refuse to obey the state. Later tempering his views with practicality, he continued to attract attention with his *State in Theory and Practice* (1935) and *Parliamentary Government in England* (1938). A scholarly and eloquent advocate of the working classes in England, Laski was one of the most influential political thinkers of his time.

FERDINAND LASSALLE (1825-1864)

Born Breslau, Germany; died Geneva, Switzerland. Orator and pamphleteer.
PLAQUE: *Cast bronze, 5" x 4⁵⁄₁₆", by I. Sors. FB 585.*

Although a profound thinker, Ferdinand Lassalle always sacrificed thought to action and is best remembered as an orator and agitator for social reform. In 1848, after the Prussian Government had dispersed the National Assembly, Lassalle used his gift of oratory to arouse the people to armed resistance. The result: a prison term and eleven years' exile from Berlin. During this period he wrote numerous pamphlets, the most important being *The Italian War and Prussia's Mission* (1859), in which Bismarck's policy was foreshadowed. But his most fruitful activity came toward the end of his life when he formed the first successful socialist party (1863), forerunner of the German Social Democratic Party. Unquestionably a rabble-rouser, he had for years urged the downcast German workers to unite in their own party to work for political and economic emancipation. Fortunately, this great advocate of social reform lived to see that party formed.

HERBERT HENRY LEHMAN (1878-   )

Born New York City. Financier and politician.
PLAQUE: *Cast bronze, diam. 7³⁄₁₆", by S. Hovell. FB 1066.*

Herbert Lehman was graduated from Williams College in 1899, was active for a time in the cotton goods business, and later became a partner in the banking house of Lehman Brothers (1908-33). During World War I he received the Distinguished Service Medal for his service to the Navy Department and on the General Staff. He acted as Governor Alfred E. Smith's campaign chairman in 1926 and as finance chairman for his Presidential campaign two years later. Lehman was lieutenant-governor of New York under Franklin D. Roosevelt (1928-32) and was the first nonfigurehead lieutenant-governor in the state's history, gaining great respect for his sweeping prison and mental hospital reforms. As Governor (1932-42) he concentrated primarily on civil defense and public welfare. Lehman has also served as Director-General of the United Nations Relief and Rehabilitation Administration (1943-46) and as United States Senator (1949-57).

URIAH PHILLIPS LEVY (1792-1862)

Born Philadelphia, Pennsylvania; died New York City. Naval officer.
PLAQUE: *Cast bronze, diam. 3¾", by L. Philip. FB 509.*

When he was ten years old Uriah P. Levy disregarded his parents' wishes and took a position as cabin boy on a coasting vessel. He served an apprenticeship, went to naval school in Philadelphia, and in 1811 became part owner and captain of the *George Washington*. The following year he joined the United States Navy and was commissioned a sailing master. During the War of 1812 Levy was captured by the British and held prisoner in England for sixteen months. Best remembered for having played a major role in the abolishment of flogging in the Navy, Levy was a courageous patriot who survived six court martials, two dismissals from the service, general anti-semitism, and dislike on the part of his peers for having risen from the ranks. In 1860 he was at last given a command.

EDWIN SAMUEL MONTAGU (1879-1924)

Born and died London, England. Politician and government official.
PLAQUE: *Cast bronze, diam. 3¹³⁄₁₆", by Kormis. FB 847.*

Edwin Samuel Montagu entered Parliament in 1906. He acted as Parliamentary Secretary to the India Office (1910-14) and quickly gained renown for his distinguished explanations to the House of Commons of proposed Indian constitutional reforms. He later served as Financial Secretary to the Treasury in Prime Minister Henry Asquith's cabinet. Instrumental in the popularizing of the first war loans and in the setting up of voluntary war-savings organizations, Montagu resigned in 1916 when David Lloyd George assumed the premiership. The following year, however, he accepted the post of Secretary of State for India. His declaration of British Indian policy, the Montagu-Chelmsford report (1917-18), contained important recommendations later made law in the Government of India Act of 1919. Montagu was dismissed from his post in 1922 for allowing the publication of Indian protests to Lloyd George's Turkish policy, but he could nonetheless lay claim to five years of great achievement in the cause of Indian self-government.

HENRY M. MORGENTHAU, JR. (1891-   )

Born New York City. Government official.
MEDAL: *Cast bronze, diam. 3", by J. R. Sinnock. FB 443.*

Henry M. Morgenthau, Jr., publisher of the *American Agriculturist* (1922-33), served both as New York State conservation commissioner and as chairman of the Governor's Agricultural Advisory Committee under Governor Franklin D. Roosevelt. When the latter assumed the Presidency of the United States (1933) he immediately named Morgenthau Chairman of the Federal Farm Board and Governor of the Federal Farm Credit Administration. The following year Morgenthau became Secretary of the Treasury. During his eleven-year tenure in that office he raised $450,000,000,000 for Government operations, the administration of New Deal projects, and the conduct of the war—a sum far exceeding that raised in the entire previous one hundred and forty-five years of the Government's existence. Morgenthau retired shortly after Roosevelt's death and served as general chairman (1947-50) and honorary chairman (1951-53) of the United Jewish Appeal. He was also chairman of the board of the American Financial and Development Corporation for Israel from 1951 to 1954.

MORDECAI MANUEL NOAH (1785-1851)

Born Philadelphia, Pennsylvania; died New York City. Journalist, playwright, and politician.
PLAQUE: *Cast bronze, 5″ x 3⅞″, by I. Sors. FB 701.*

Mordecai Manuel Noah worked for the United States Treasury and, when the national capital was moved to Washington in 1800, served as a reporter in the Pennsylvania legislature. He later moved to Charleston, South Carolina, and in 1813 was appointed consul to Tunis. Although his commission was revoked shortly after he arrived there, he did effect the release of Americans held captive by the Algerian pirates. Noah was the author of several successful plays; served as editor of the *National Advocate* (1817-27), a Tammany newspaper in New York City; and later founded and edited two other journals there. He was sheriff of New York in 1822 and surveyor of the Port of New York from 1829 to 1833. His plan to establish a Jewish colony, "Ararat," on Grand Island in the Niagara River came to naught, but in a brief moment of triumph he did lay a cornerstone there. *Gleanings from a Gathered Harvest* (1845) is a collection of Noah's newspaper essays.

MAX NORDAU (1849-1923)

Born Budapest, Hungary; died Paris, France. Physician, journalist, and social philosopher.
PLAQUE: *Cast bronze, 4¼″ x 3¾″, by I. Sors. FB 547.*

Max Nordau (né Südfeld) began the practice of medicine in Paris in 1882, simultaneously pursuing a highly successful career in journalism. Upon reading the manuscript of Theodor Herzl's *Jewish State* he became an ardent Zionist. He soon was Herzl's most trusted and loyal adviser and was vice-president of the first six Zionist congresses. Convinced that Jews could never be a real part of European civilization, he wrote numerous articles justifying Zionism to non-Jews and assimilationists. He demanded an autonomous Jewish state and was dismayed in his last years at the eagerness of Zionist leaders to accept a Jewish colony in Turkish Palestine. Nordau was particularly famous for his *Conventional Lies of Our Civilization* (1883), in which he blamed nineteenth-century social unrest on the hypocrisy of civilization itself, and for his *Degeneration* (two volumes, 1893), in which he discussed contemporary art as being a manifestation of a diseased society.

LEON PINSKER (1821-1891)

Born Tomashov, Poland; died Odessa, Russia. Physician and writer.
PLAQUE: *Cast bronze, diam. 3⅞″, by I. Sors. FB 706.*

Leon Pinsker received his medical degree from the University of Moscow and soon became one of the leading physicians of his day. But it is as an essayist and pamphleteer that he is best known. A frequent contributor to the Russian Jewish weekly *Rassviet,* and later to the periodical *Zion,* Pinsker was an advocate of russianization and general assimilation. He was one of the first to demand the translation into Russian of the Bible and the prayerbook. After the pogrom of Easter 1871, however, he abruptly reversed his position and published a widely read pamphlet calling for the self-emancipation of Russian Jews and the establishment of a Jewish nation. The last twenty years of his life were devoted to convincing his fellow Jews that they would always be aliens and that the only solution was a "spiritual center," a homeland where they might live as a nation upon their own soil.

WALTHER RATHENAU (1867-1922)

Born and died Berlin, Germany. Engineer, statesman, and social philosopher.
PLAQUE: *Cast bronze, diam. 4⁷⁄₁₆″, by B. Elkan. FB 151.*

Walther Rathenau received his doctorate (1889) through his thesis on light absorption by metals and shortly thereafter discovered a method of producing chlorine and alkalis by electrolysis. In 1899 he joined his father's electric company, rapidly guiding it to a position as one of the three largest concerns in Germany. Rathenau was an ardent patriot and established the War Materials Section of the War Office, thus permitting Germany to continue the First World War despite her deplorable economic condition. In 1921 he negotiated the Treaty of Wiesbaden with France, whereby a large portion of reparations were to be paid with raw materials. In 1922 he became Foreign Minister of the Weimar Republic and was assassinated by terrorists for his insistence that reparations be paid. A man of high ethical standards, Rathenau felt that society was in need of radical change. Among his works are *In Days to Come* (1917) and *The New Society* (1919).

HERBERT LOUIS SAMUEL, 1st Viscount Samuel
(1870-1963)

Born Liverpool; died London, England. Statesman.
PLAQUE: *Cast bronze, diam. 4¼", by Kormis. FB 717.*

Herbert Samuel was educated at the University of Oxford and in 1902 was elected to Parliament. As Parliamentary Undersecretary to the Home Office (1905-09) he established the probation and juvenile court systems in Great Britain. He later served as Postmaster-General (1910-16) and Home Secretary (1916) in Prime Minister Henry Asquith's cabinet. Samuel was not a Zionist, but he nonetheless contributed greatly to mutual understanding between the Zionists and the British Government at a time when such understanding was most necessary. He helped to secure the Balfour Declaration in 1917 and three years later was named first High Commissioner of Palestine (1920-25). A truly great mediator with an uncanny ability to get others to compromise, Samuel was leader of the Liberal Party in the House of Commons (1931-35) and, after his elevation to the peerage (1937), in the House of Lords (1944-55). Lord Samuel was always known for his unwillingness to sacrifice principle under any circumstances and his philosophy was expressed in such works as *The Tree of Good and Evil* (1933), *Practical Politics* (1935), and *Belief and Action* (1937).

[67]

MOSHE SHARETT (1894-)

Born Kherson, Russia. Statesman.
PLAQUE: *Cast bronze, 5⁹⁄₁₆″ x 4⁷⁄₁₆″, by Kormis. FB 909.*

Moshe Sharett emigrated to Palestine in 1906. He carefully learned the language and mores of the Arabs among whom he lived, later studied law in Istanbul, and served in the Turkish army during World War I. After the war he went to England as an adviser to Chaim Weizmann on Arab affairs. In 1924, however, he returned to his adopted homeland, where he became a staff member of the daily newspaper *Davar.* Sharett assisted in the establishment of the Jewish brigade that fought in World War II. In 1946 he moved to the United States in order to enlist support for the soon-to-be-established State of Israel and later was largely responsible for acquiring official recognition for the new state from other nations throughout the world. He served as Israel's first Minister of Foreign Affairs and, upon David Ben-Gurion's retirement in 1953, assumed the post of Prime Minister. Two years later his predecessor returned to office, and Sharett became a member of the Knesset, an office that he holds to this day.

OSCAR SOLOMON STRAUS (1850-1926)

Born Otterberg, Germany; died New York City. Merchant and diplomat.
PLAQUE: *Cast bronze, diam. 6⁵⁄₁₆″, by A. Eisenberg. FB 449.*

For a brief period after receiving his A.B. (1871) and LL.B. (1873) from Columbia University, Oscar Straus worked for his father in the import business. A scholar of some distinction, he gained national attention in 1886 as author of *The Origin of the Republican Form of Government in the United States.* The following year he was appointed Minister to Turkey. His career in that post tells the history of American-Turkish relations between 1887 and 1910, for so successful was he that he was twice recalled in time of crisis to represent America in Constantinople (Minister, 1887-89 and 1898-1900; Ambassador, 1909-10). Straus was a member of the Permanent Court of International Arbitration at The Hague (1902, 1908, 1912, and 1920) and served as Secretary of Commerce and Labor in President Theodore Roosevelt's cabinet (1906-09). He was the author of *Roger Williams* (1894), *The United States Doctrine of Citizenship* (1901), and *The American Spirit* (1913).

HENRIETTA SZOLD (1860-1945)

Born Baltimore, Maryland; died Jerusalem, Palestine. Social worker.
PLAQUE: *Cast bronze, diam. 4¼", by Kormis. FB 1013.*

Henrietta Szold began her career in social work when, while teaching in a fashionable girls' school, she spent her evenings conducting classes for newly arrived immigrants. Although a charter member of the National Council of Jewish Women, Miss Szold's greatest interest was Hadassah, which she transformed into a national organization. She annually toured the country in its behalf and in 1926 was named honorary president. In 1917, at the request of Justice Louis Brandeis, she organized the American Zionist Medical Unit, thus furthering the original goal of Hadassah by improving health conditions in Palestine. Upon her first trip to the Holy Land in 1909, Miss Szold had written: "If not Zionism, then nothing." It was fitting, therefore, that eighteen years later she became the first woman to be named to the Zionist Executive. Miss Szold's later years were crowned by what may well have been her greatest contribution to humanity: her organization and immediate supervision of the Youth Aliyah, a movement providing for the emigration, resettlement, and education of youths threatened by the Nazi regime.

LEON TROTSKY (1879-1940)

Born near Elizavetgrad, Russia; died Mexico City, Mexico. Politician and journalist.
PLAQUE: *Cast bronze, 5¾" x 5⅛", by I. Sors. FB 486.*

Lev Davidovich Bronstein was arrested as a revolutionary in 1898. Four years later he assumed the name of Leon Trotsky and escaped to London, where he collaborated with Nikolai Lenin in planning the Communist Revolution. Temporarily triumphant, he returned to Russia in 1905 and was elected to the St. Petersburg Soviet of Workers' Deputies. The entire soviet was arrested that year, however, and once again Trotsky fled his homeland. First in Vienna and later in Paris he worked for revolutionist newspapers. But he was soon expelled from France and came to America as editor of *Novy Mir (The New World)*, remaining in this country until the successful Revolution of 1917. Thereupon he returned to Russia and served as Commissar for Foreign Affairs and Commissar of War, positions second only to that of Lenin. Shortly after Lenin's death in 1923, Trotsky's practical and ideological adversary, Josef Stalin, exiled him for "anti-party activities." Trotsky went first to Turkey, then to Norway, and finally settled in Mexico City, where in 1940 he was assassinated by a Stalinist agent.

JOSEPH TRUMPELDOR (1880-1920)

Born Pyatigorsk, Russia; died Tel Hai, Palestine. Army officer and socialist-Zionist leader.

PLAQUE: *Cast bronze, 2¹³⁄₁₆″ x 1¹¹⁄₁₆″, by B. Schatz. FB 132.*

Joseph Trumpeldor entered the Russian Army in 1902 and in 1904 lost an arm in the siege of Port Arthur in the Russo-Japanese War. During the following year, while being held as a captive, he conducted a school for his fellow prisoners and formulated a plan for a communal settlement in Palestine. Upon his return to Russia he was made the first Jewish officer in the Imperial Army. After years of planning, he established an agricultural settlement in Migdal, Palestine, and later served as a farm worker in Dagania. In 1915 he left the country in order to aid Vladimir Jabotinsky in his formation of a Jewish military unit. After the war he lived in England and Russia. He helped to establish the Jewish Legion, and he returned to Palestine to organize a self-defense movement against the Arabs. He was killed in the Arab conquest of Tel Hai and overnight became an inspirational legend that helped to keep Jewish hopes alive for the next quarter-century.

BARUCH CHARNEY VLADECK (1886-1938)

Born Minsk, Russia; died New York City. Journalist and community leader.

PLAQUE: *Cast bronze, diam. 5¹¹⁄₁₆″, by A. Eisenberg. FB 763.*

Baruch Charney assumed the name of B. Charney Vladeck when he began his revolutionary activities in Russia shortly after the turn of the century. He was imprisoned following the Revolution of 1905 but three years later fled to America, where he accepted a position as manager of the Philadelphia branch of the *Jewish Daily Forward*. After studies at the University of Pennsylvania, he went to New York in 1915 and within two years became a member of the Board of Aldermen. Vladeck, a socialist, was a major figure in the Jewish labor movement and, as general manager of the *Forward* (1921-38), a leader in the fight against Nazism and Communism. He was appointed a member of the New York Housing Authority by Mayor Fiorello LaGuardia and helped to establish the first public housing in New York—the realization of a proposal outlined by Vladeck as early as 1917.

CHAIM WEIZMANN (1874-1952)

Born Motol, Russia; died Rehovot, Israel. Chemist, educator, and statesman.
PLAQUE: *Cast bronze, diam. 4⁷⁄₁₆″, by Kormis. FB 415.*

Chaim Weizmann, educated at the Universities of Berlin and Freiburg, was lecturer in chemistry at the University of Geneva (1901-04) and reader in biochemistry at the University of Manchester (1904-16). While Director of the British Admiralty Laboratories (1916-19) he discovered a process for synthesizing acetone used in the manufacture of high explosives, thus greatly contributing to the final Allied victory in World War I. Weizmann was an early follower of Theodor Herzl, but after the second Zionist congress (1898) he renounced diplomacy as the program for Zionism and demanded cultural work and colonization in its stead. Later he was largely responsible for the 1917 Balfour Declaration promising Palestine as a Jewish national home. Weizmann was president of the World Zionist Organization (1920-31; 1935-46) and of the Jewish Agency for Palestine (1929-31; 1935-46). In 1932 he was named president of the board of governors of the Hebrew University and in 1934 assumed the directorship of the Daniel Sieff Research Institute (now the Weizmann Institute of Science), a position he held until his death. Weizmann, a brilliant chemist and teacher, was also a great humanitarian and the people's choice for first President of Israel (1948-52).

DAVID WOLFFSOHN (1856-1914)

Born Dorbiany, Lithuania; died Homburg, Germany. Merchant.
PLAQUE: *Cast bronze, 5⅛" x 4⅛₆", by I. Sors. FB 867.*

In 1872 David Wolffsohn fled to East Prussia in order to escape
military duty. At first he failed in business, but he became a partner
in a timber firm in Papenburg that quickly prospered. As it did so
Wolffsohn began to devote more and more of his time and attention
to Jewish affairs. He was a close friend and adviser of Theodor Herzl,
and, as the financial genius behind the Zionist movement, helped to
set up the Jewish Colonial Trust in London (1898). He served as
its administrator until his death. Wolffsohn was an unyielding political
Zionist and was bitterly opposed by the practical Zionists who wanted
immediate colonization. But he nonetheless managed to serve as
intermediary between Herzl and his opponents both within and
without the movement and was elected president of the seventh
through tenth Zionist congresses (1905-11). The library at the
Hebrew University, built with funds bequeathed by Wolffsohn, was
dedicated in his name in 1930.

Law

GREAT JEWISH PORTRAITS IN METAL

LOUIS DEMBITZ BRANDEIS (1856-1941)

Born Louisville, Kentucky; died Washington, D.C. Jurist.
PLAQUE: *Cast zinc, 6⅝″ x 5½″, by A. Eisenberg. FB 421.*

Louis Brandeis received his LL.B. from Harvard University in 1877. He began practice in Boston, where he shortly became known for his extraordinary knowledge and thoroughness. Brandeis believed in the flexibility of the law, demanding its constant reinterpretation lest the people become slaves to tradition. He was a champion of the small businessman, fought the large corporations, and was influential in the passage of minimum wage legislation. As Associate Justice of the United States Supreme Court (1916-39) Brandeis usually found himself in the minority, yet he lived to see many of his farsighted views upheld in later decisions. Common sense and fairness were his criteria. After 1910 Brandeis was an ardent Zionist and was honorary president of the Zionist Organization of America (1918-21) and of the World Zionist Organization (1920-21).

BENJAMIN NATHAN CARDOZO (1870-1938)

Born New York City; died Port Chester, New York. Jurist.
PLAQUE: *Cast zinc, 7⁵⁄₁₆" x 5⅞", by Mostel. FB 642.*

Benjamin Cardozo was graduated from Columbia University in 1889 and two years later (sans law degree) was admitted to the bar. Acting primarily as counsel for other lawyers he soon gained a brilliant reputation among his peers. He was elected Justice of the New York Supreme Court in 1913, but six weeks later the Judges of the Court of Appeals asked the Governor to allow Cardozo to serve with them. Appointed a temporary member, he was elected a regular member in 1917 (Chief Judge, 1926). Cardozo, a master of common law, made the Court of Appeals the second most distinguished tribunal in the land. Named Oliver Wendell Holmes' successor as Associate Justice of the United States Supreme Court (1932), he became in six short years one of its immortals. Cardozo was author of the classic *Nature of the Judicial Process* (1921), *The Growth of the Law* (1924), and *Law and Literature* (1931).

ADOLPHE (ISAAC MOÏSE) CRÉMIEUX (1796-1880)

Born Nîmes, France; died Paris, France. Lawyer and statesman.
MEDAL: *Cast bronze, gilded, diam. 2¾", by A. Bovrel. FB 137.*

Adolphe Crémieux was admitted to the bar in 1817 and soon won national fame for his eloquence and extraordinary legal knowledge. In 1840 he went with Sir Moses Montefiore to Damascus in order to defend the Jews there who were accused of having committed ritual murder. Achieving the impossible, he won their acquittal, returned to Paris in triumph, and was elected deputy in 1842. Crémieux helped to incite the Revolution of 1848 by his brilliant oratory and was elected a member of the provisional Government. As Minister of Justice he abolished the death penalty for political offenders and introduced trial by jury. Holding the same post twenty years later (1870-71), he secured the emancipation of Algerian Jews. Among his greatest accomplishments was the abolishment of the Oath More Judaica, which French Jews had been forced to take before testifying in court. Crémieux was a founder of the Alliance Israélite Universelle and was its president (1863-66; 1868-80).

FELIX FRANKFURTER (1882-   )

Born Vienna, Austria. Jurist.
PLAQUE: *Cast bronze, diam. 5½", by A. Eisenberg. FB 764.*

Felix Frankfurter, who was brought to this country at the age of twelve, was educated in the New York public schools and graduated from the Harvard Law School in 1906. He served in the Justice and War Departments and, from 1914 to 1939, was professor of law at Harvard University. As a young man he became associated with the Zionist Organization of America and served as legal adviser to the Zionist delegation at the Versailles Peace Conference in 1919. Frankfurter was an Associate Justice of the United States Supreme Court from 1939 to 1962. He is the author and editor of numerous books, the best known of which are a study of the Sacco-Vanzetti case (1927) and *The Public and Its Government* (1930). A collection of his opinions was published in 1949 under the title *The Constitutional World of Mr. Justice Frankfurter.*

RUFUS DANIEL ISAACS, 1st Marquess of Reading
(1860-1935)

Born and died London, England. Jurist, politician, and government official.
PLAQUE: *Cast bronze, diam. 9¹⁄₁₆″, by A. Lowenthal. FB 154.*

Rufus Daniel Isaacs entered the legal profession in 1887 and within
a decade was the youngest man ever to become queen's counsel. He
was elected to Parliament in 1904, worked untiringly for the establishment of the Court of Criminal Appeal, and was made Solicitor-
General in 1910 and Lord Chief Justice of England three years later.
Isaacs was known as a deadly opponent in a legal dispute, but was
the most humane of jurists. As Viceroy and Governor-General of
India (1921-26) he faced the unyielding opposition of Mahatma
Gandhi, whom he was finally obliged to imprison for inciting mass
civil disobedience. But against almost insuperable odds Isaacs did
sow the seeds of self-government throughout the greater part of India.
Upon his return to England he was raised to the peerage. Among
the many posts held by the Marquess of Reading during his long
career were the Ambassadorship to the United States (1918) and
the Secretaryship of State for Foreign Affairs (1931).

IRVING LEHMAN (1876-1945)

Born New York City; died Port Chester, New York. Jurist.
PLAQUE: *Cast bronze, 5⁹⁄₁₆″ x 4⅛″, by I. Sors. FB 487.*

Irving Lehman, brother of Senator Lehman, received his A.B. from
Columbia University in 1896 (LL.B., 1898) and was a practicing
lawyer for ten years. He rapidly gained a reputation as one of the
most brilliant and able attorneys in New York and was elected to the
State Supreme Court at the age of thirty-two. After serving in that
capacity for sixteen years (1908-24), he was named Associate Justice
of the State Court of Appeals in 1924 and Chief Justice after 1939.
Lehman believed in the utter flexibility of the law and was nationally
known for his liberal, farsighted opinions. He was, for example, the
first jurist in the land to accept the legality of minimum wage legislation. He was active in Jewish affairs and was a member of the
Jewish Welfare Board, a governor of the American Friends of Hebrew
University, and a member of the board of governors of The Jewish
Theological Seminary of America.

LOUIS MARSHALL (1856-1929)

*Born Syracuse, New York; died Zürich, Switzerland. Lawyer and
philanthropist.*
PLAQUE: *Cast zinc, diam. 4⁹⁄₁₆″, by Mantel. FB 425.*

Louis Marshall, a graduate of Columbia University law school, practiced in Syracuse (1878-94) and New York City (1894-1929).
He was one of America's foremost constitutional lawyers, being no-
tably active in the formation and revision of New York law as a
member of the constitutional conventions of 1890, 1894, and 1915.
In 1911, as a consequence of Russia's refusal to allow American Jews
to enter the country, he effected the abrogation of the Russo-American
treaty of 1832. As founder and president (1912-29) of the American
Jewish Committee he sought liberal immigration laws and, as a delegate to the Versailles Peace Conference (1919), he led in the fight
for the inclusion of minority rights clauses in the treaty. He was a
founder of the Jewish Welfare Board, chairman of the American
Jewish Relief Committee, and chairman of the board of The Jewish
Theological Seminary of America (1904-29). For twenty years Marshall was spokesman for and undisputed leader of American Jewry.

HORACE STERN (1878-   )

Born Philadelphia, Pennsylvania. Jurist.
PLAQUE: *Cast bronze, 5¾″ x 3⅞″, by Mantel. FB 506.*

Horace Stern was graduated from the University of Pennsylvania in 1899 and admitted to the bar three years later. He lectured at the law school of his alma mater from 1902 to 1917, and after a highly successful career in the practice of law he was appointed to the Court of Common Pleas in 1920. Noted for his liberal views, Stern served with great distinction as Presiding Judge of that court (1924-35). He was then elected to the Supreme Court of Pennsylvania in 1935, where he has been Chief Justice since 1952. A large portion of his time has been devoted to Jewish causes. He has served as vice-president both of the Jewish Publication Society and of Dropsie College and has been a director and honorary president of the Federation of Jewish Charities in Philadelphia. Stern is a man of great erudition; his opinions have often become examples for the legal profession as a whole.

MAYER SULZBERGER (1843-1923)

Born Heidelsheim, Germany; died Philadelphia, Pennsylvania. Jurist.
PLAQUE: *Cast bronze, 5⅛″ x 3⁵⁄₁₆″, by Mantel. FB 599.*

Mayer Sulzberger studied law under Moses Dropsie and was admitted to the bar in 1865. He was appointed to the Philadelphia Court of Common Pleas thirty years later (Presiding Judge, 1902-15) and soon gained fame as a man of great wit and erudition. Although never a member of an appellate court and thus not writing opinions of final authority, he was one of the best known jurists in America. Sulzberger, a highly original thinker and scholar, was the author of *The Am ha-Arets, the Ancient Hebrew Parliament* (1909), *The Polity of the Ancient Hebrews* (1912), *The Ancient Hebrew Law of Homicide* (1915), and *The Status of Labor in Ancient Israel* (1923). He was also a founder and first president of the American Jewish Committee. Sulzberger possessed a superb collection of Hebrew manuscripts and incunabula which in 1902 he donated to The Jewish Theological Seminary of America. This gift included what later became the nucleus of the collection of The Jewish Museum.

Business
&
Finance

GREAT JEWISH PORTRAITS IN METAL

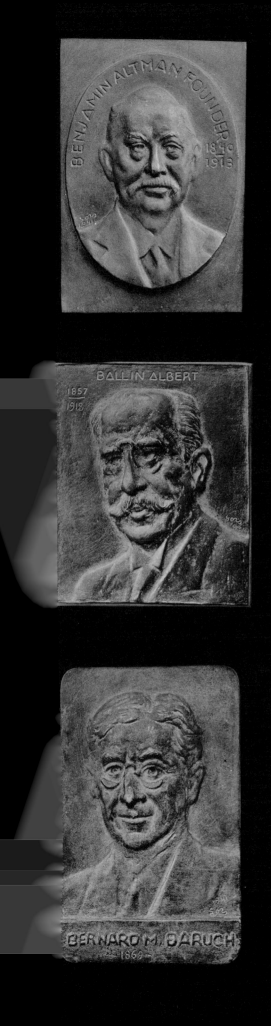

BENJAMIN ALTMAN (1840-1913)

Born and died New York City. Merchant, philanthropist, and art patron.
PLAQUE: *Cast bronze, 5⁵⁄₁₆″ x 3¾″, by I. Sors. FB 581.*

After years of working in dry goods stores in New York City and
Newark, B. Altman opened his own establishment in 1865. Through
his great ability and determination, it gradually became one of the
finest stores in New York and soon Altman had the time and capital
to indulge his great interest in art. Beginning with Chinese porcelains
and enamels, his collection eventually included paintings, furniture,
tapestries, sculpture, porcelains, and enamels valued at $20,000,000.
Upon Altman's death the entire collection, one of the greatest private
fortunes in art ever assembled, was given to the Metropolitan Museum
in New York. Altman also willed a substantial sum of money to the
National Academy of Design for the promotion of American painting.
At first somewhat of a dilettante, Altman was not content with merely
collecting; over the years he also developed a very considerable knowledge of art in all its forms.

ALBERT BALLIN (1857-1918)

Born and died Hamburg, Germany. Shipowner.
PLAQUE: *Cast bronze, 4⅜″ x 3¾″, by I. Sors. FB 542.*

Albert Ballin was chief passenger agent for the English Carr Line
when it merged with the Hamburg-Amerika Line. He served as a
director of the new company, and under his guidance it soon became
Germany's largest shipping concern. He established the first fast
steamer service between Hamburg and America, introduced the first
pleasure cruises on German ships, and was the first to combine large-
scale freight and passenger transportation on the same vessel. Ballin
was one of Kaiser Wilhelm's most trusted advisers in the realms of
maritime and economic affairs. He achieved international recognition
by negotiating important agreements designed to eliminate wasteful
competition among shipping lines. However, despondent over the out-
come of World War I and the consequent destruction of his life's work,
Ballin committed suicide in 1918.

BERNARD MANNES BARUCH (1870-   )

Born Camden, South Carolina. Financier, statesman, and philanthropist.
PLAQUE: *Cast bronze, 5⁹⁄₁₆″ x 3⁹⁄₁₆″, by I. Sors. FB 528.*

Bernard Baruch was graduated from the City College of New York
in 1889. Within but a few years he had become a partner in a brokerage firm and a very prominent member of the New York Stock
Exchange. In 1916 President Woodrow Wilson appointed Baruch to
the advisory committee of the Council of National Defense. Other
appointments followed, the most important of which was that of
Chairman of the War Industries Board (1918-19). Baruch was

also a member of the Supreme Economic Council of the Paris Peace Conference (1919) and of the President's Conference for Capital and Labor. In recognition of his services he has been given the Distinguished Service Medal and many other governmental and academic honors, not least of which was the naming of his alma mater's business school The Bernard Baruch School of Business. He has gained special fame for his role as friend and adviser to several presidents and statesmen.

MOSES AARON DROPSIE (1821-1905)

Born and died Philadelphia, Pennsylvania. Lawyer, businessman, educator, and philanthropist.
PLAQUE: *Cast zinc, 5¼" x 3¾", by Mantel. FB 434.*

Moses Dropsie was a businessman for several years before studying law and being admitted to the bar in 1851. He retained his keen interest in business however. The president of a number of railroads and organizer of the Philadelphia street railway system, he early became one of that city's foremost citizens. In 1856 he helped to found the Republican Party in Pennsylvania. Born of a mixed marriage, Dropsie chose to follow Judaism when he was fourteen and remained a devout Jew throughout his life. He was president of the Philadelphia chapter of the Alliance Israélite Universelle (1883-1905) and a founder and president (1862-70; 1889-92) of the Hebrew Education Society. Dropsie was president also of Maimonides College (1867-73) and Gratz College (1893-1905). On his death the bulk of his estate was bequeathed for the establishment of Dropsie College for Hebrew and Cognate Learning, one of the first educational institutions to have no entrance requirements as to creed, color, or sex.

ABRAHAM FURTADO (1756-1816)

Born London, England; died Bordeaux, France. Merchant and statesman.
PLAQUE: *Cast bronze, 6⅝" x 5", by I. Sors. FB 775.*

Abraham Furtado was born of a Portuguese Marrano family. His mother had fled Lisbon after the death of her husband in the famous earthquake of 1755 and, soon after the birth of her son, she settled in Bordeaux. Furtado was first a merchant and later became a very successful dealer in real estate. He was a member of a commission convened by Malesherbes in 1788 to study proposals for the amelioration of the condition of the Jews in France. Five years later his support of the moderate Girondists effected his exile and the confiscation of his property, but within a year he returned and resumed his business. In 1806, when Napoleon summoned one hundred leading Jews for consultation concerning their integration into French life, Furtado was chosen president of the group, which became known as the "Assembly of Notables." One of the most prominent French Jews of his time, Furtado served as vice-mayor of Bordeaux for many years.

ADAM GIMBEL (1817-1896)

Born Bavaria, Germany; died Philadelphia, Pennsylvania. Merchant.
PLAQUE: *Cast bronze, diam. 5¾″, by I. Sors. FB 743.*

Adam Gimbel arrived in the United States in 1835 and became a peddler throughout the Mississippi Valley. Cognizant of the many needs of the small western communities, after seven years of traveling among them he opened a general store in Vincennes, Indiana. He prospered there and inspired his sons to expand the family business. With his encouragement they opened a store in Danville, Illinois, in the early 1880's. They failed in this, however, and in 1889 moved to Milwaukee, where they opened the first truly modern department store. So successful were they that five years later they were enabled to add a store in Philadelphia to their growing enterprise and soon had major department stores in New York, Pittsburgh, and Chicago as well. By 1930 Gimbel Brothers, Inc., which had started ninety years before as Adam Gimbel's general store in the wilds of Indiana, had become the largest organization of its kind in the world.

Baron MAURICE de HIRSCH (1831-1896)

Born Munich, Germany; died Ersek-Ujvar, Hungary. Banker and philanthropist.
PLAQUE: *Cast zinc, 5⅜″ x 3⅞″, by I. Sors. FB 673.*

Baron Maurice de Hirsch, who was born into a very prominent Jewish family, first gained renown by acquiring the rights to build a railroad through the Balkans to Constantinople, thus bringing to fulfillment the long-debated plan to link East and West. While in Turkey, he noted the horrible condition of Jews in the Orient and gave funds in their behalf to the Alliance Israélite Universelle. When his offer of fifty million francs to train Jews in industry and agriculture was refused by the Russian Government, Hirsch formed the Jewish Colonization Association for the resettlement of Russian Jews. He also established funds to promote vocational training for Galician Jews and for Jewish immigrants to America and Canada. During the Russo-Turkish War he maintained hospitals for both armies. Unequalled in his humanitarianism, Hirsch is believed to have given over $100,000,000 in his lifelong efforts to improve conditions throughout the world.

OTTO HERMAN KAHN (1867-1934)

Born Mannheim, Germany; died New York City. Financier, philanthropist, and art patron.

PLAQUE: *Cast bronze, 6¹⁄₁₆″ x 4¹³⁄₁₆″, by I. Sors. FB 562.*

Otto Kahn had been engaged in banking in Berlin and London before he came to America in 1893. Four years later he joined the firm of Kuhn, Loeb and Company and soon emerged as a giant among giants. In 1903 he became a stockholder in the floundering Metropolitan Opera Company and subsequently was co-owner of it with William K. Vanderbilt. Together they reorganized it and launched its Golden Age when in 1908 they hired Giulio Gatti-Casazza as general manager and Arturo Toscanini as musical director. Kahn was president of the Metropolitan from 1918 to 1931. Since many of his philanthropic activities were pursued in secret, their full extent will doubtless never be known. Not until 1930, for example, was it learned that he had long given monetary prizes to promising Negro singers. Kahn donated both money and art treasures to museums throughout America as well as generous aid toward the restoration of the Parthenon in Athens.

ADOLPH LEWISOHN (1849-1938)

Born Hamburg, Germany; died Saranac Lake, New York. Financier and philanthropist.

PLAQUE: *Cast bronze, 5¼″ x 4¼″, by I. Sors. FB 805.*

Adolph Lewisohn emigrated to the United States in 1867 and joined his brothers in a very successful copper mining operation. It is as a humanitarian, however, that he is best remembered. President of the Hebrew Sheltering Guardian Society for more than thirty years, he worked untiringly in the fields of child welfare and prison reform, demanding fair wages for prison labor and proper sanitary conditions for inmates. In 1913 he donated the Lewisohn Stadium to the City College of New York; it has since become a major feature of New York's cultural life. Lewisohn was a founder of the Federation for the Support of Jewish Philanthropic Societies in New York and gave generously to Mount Sinai Hospital, the Hebrew Technical School for Girls, and Johns Hopkins and Columbia Universities. In two final acts of munificence he bequeathed his art collection to the Brooklyn Museum and his home to the City College to serve as a social center.

GRACIA MENDESIA (MENDES) (1510-1569)

Born Portugal; died Constantinople, Turkey. Philanthropist.
MEDAL: *Cast bronze, diam. 3½", by Pasterino. FB 77.* (NOTE: *It is uncertain whether this fine Renaissance medal represents this Gracia Mendesia or her niece of the same name.*)

Gracia Mendesia, born into a well-known family of bankers, was forced to flee the Inquisition in 1536. She settled in Antwerp and quickly became known as the "angel of the Marranos," much of her time, energy, and fortune being spent on the resettlement and protection of her fellow Jews. In 1549, threatened with the confiscation of her property, she fled to Venice. When her secret advocacy of Judaism became known to the authorities, Señora Mendesia was imprisoned. But the Turkish Sultan, hoping that she would bring her great wealth to his country, intervened on her behalf and she was released. She then spent two years in Ferrara and, upon the restoration of her property, removed to Constantinople. Permitted to continue her many benefactions unhindered (among them the construction of a synagogue), she remained there until her death. Gracia Mendesia was one of the most self-sacrificing philanthropists ever known. Not only did she give of her wealth but, at the risk of her own life, she also effected the rescue of many Sephardic refugees who, without her aid, would almost certainly have been killed.

ALFRED MORITZ MOND, Lord Melchett (1868-1930)

Born Farnworth, England; died London, England. Industrialist and politician.

PLAQUE: *Cast bronze, diam. 5⅟₁₆″, by Kormis. FB 846.*

Alfred Mond studied law at the Universities of Cambridge and Edinburgh and later entered his father's firm, Brunner, Mond and Company, the world's largest producer of alkali. He served as chairman of the board of that company and also organized and headed the Imperial Chemical Industries, Ltd., one of the most powerful trusts in the world. Mond was a brilliant industrialist and one of the first European businessmen to encourage mass production and relaxed business-labor relations. The result was a maintained level of output without which England might well have been unable to conduct World War I. Mond, a member both of Parliament (1906-28) and of Lloyd George's cabinet (1916-22), was active in world Jewish affairs as chairman of the British Economic Board for Palestine and president of the English Keren Hayesod Committee and the Zionist Federation of Great Britain. He was elevated to the peerage in 1928.

Sir MOSES MONTEFIORE (1784-1885)

Born Leghorn, Italy; died Ramsgate, England. Financier and philanthropist.
MEDAL: *Cast bronze, diam. 1¾″, by H. B. Salef. FB 432.*

Sir Moses Montefiore emigrated to England as a young man and quickly amassed a great fortune as a member of the London Stock Exchange. He retired in 1824, however, and devoted the rest of his life to Jewish causes throughout the world. In 1840 he persuaded the Sultan to grant Jews the same rights and privileges as were accorded aliens in the Ottoman Empire. Six years later he accomplished the revocation of the ukase of 1844 ordering Jews to leave the western frontier of Russia. In 1864 he went with a British naval escort to Morocco to subdue a violent outbreak of antisemitism. These are but a few vivid examples of Montefiore's sixty-year fight for the rights of Jews. Sir Moses, knighted in 1837 and made a baronet nine years later, was president of the Board of Deputies of British Jews from 1838 to 1874.

HENRY M. MORGENTHAU, SR. (1856-1946)

Born Mannheim, Germany; died New York City. Financier and diplomat.
PLAQUE: *Cast bronze, 6³⁄₁₆″ x 4½″, by I. Sors. FB 460.*

Henry Morgenthau attended the City College of New York and received his LL.B. from Columbia University in 1877. He relinquished a very successful law practice to enter the field of real estate as president of the Central Realty Bond Company (1899-1905) and later as founder and president of the Henry Morgenthau Company (1905-13). He was chairman of the finance committees of the Democratic National Committees of 1912 and 1916 and United States Ambassador to Turkey from 1913 to 1916. At the outbreak of World War I Morgenthau assumed complete charge of the interests of nine belligerent nations and made a successful appeal on behalf of the Jewish colonists in Palestine, who had been reduced to great want by the stern military governor, Djemal Pasha. Morgenthau was an incorporator of the Red Cross and vice-chairman of Near East Relief, Inc. (1919-21). He also served both on a commission to investigate conditions in Poland (1919) and as chairman of the Greek Refugee Settlement Commission (1923).

ADOLPH SIMON OCHS (1858-1935)

Born Cincinnati, Ohio; died New York City. Journalist and philanthropist.
PLAQUE: *Cast bronze, 5¼″ x 3⁹⁄₁₆″, by Mantel. FB 762.*

Adolph Ochs was a newsboy and printer's devil in Knoxville, Tennessee, when at the age of eighteen he moved to Chattanooga and helped to found the *Chattanooga Daily Dispatch.* When the paper failed, he paid all debts and merged with the *Chattanooga Times,* of which he later gained ownership and control. Under his leadership it became one of the most influential journals in the South. In 1896 Ochs bought into the financially unstable *New York Times* and by 1899 was sole owner. Ochs's greatest contribution to American journalism was his insistence on complete news coverage totally separated from all editorial opinion. Adhering to his policies, the *Times* remains America's foremost newspaper more than a quarter-century after his death. Ochs underwrote the preparation of the *Dictionary of American Biography* (1925) and was chairman of a committee that raised $5,000,000 (of which he gave one-sixth) for the Hebrew Union College. He also instituted the annual *Times* fund for New York's "One Hundred Neediest Cases."

JOSEPH SÜSS OPPENHEIMER (1698-1738)

Born Heidelberg, Germany; died Stuttgart, Germany. Financier.
MEDAL: *Lead, diam. 1¼″, artist unknown (Stuttgart, 18th century). FB 68.*

Joseph Oppenheimer, known as Jud Süss (Jew Süss), held numerous jobs in Germany and Austria and in 1732 became mint-master in Darmstadt. He held the post of private treasurer to Prince (later Duke) Karl Alexander of Württemberg and was made that petty monarch's sole confidential adviser in 1734. Oppenheimer had total control over the royal mint and used his great financial knowledge and skill to accomplish the impossible: making the duke independent of gifts from his subjects. As a result, he was accused by the nobles of every possible financial crime, for since the duke was no longer subsidized by them they were no longer his master. But Oppenheimer was regularly vindicated by auditors' reports. However, in retaliation for his great success, he was finally imprisoned with the entire Jewish population of Stuttgart on the very night that his patron died. He refused to accept Christianity and was hanged shortly thereafter.

JOSEPH PULITZER (1847-1911)

Born Mako, Hungary; died Charleston, South Carolina. Journalist and philanthropist.
PLAQUE: *Cast bronze, 6⅟₁₆″ x 4⅛″, by I. Sors. FB 498.*

In search of adventure, Joseph Pulitzer came to America in 1864 and joined the Union Army. After the war he settled in St. Louis, where he went to work for the German daily, *Westliche Post*. Within but a few years Pulitzer was a police commissioner, an underage (twenty-two) member of the Missouri House of Representatives, and secretary of the convention that nominated Horace Greeley for the Presidency (1872). In 1878 he bought the *St. Louis Dispatch* and merged it with the *Post*. Successful in this venture, he moved to New York, bought the *World* (1883), and made it into one of America's most fearless and independent daily newspapers. Pulitzer's interest in the furtherance of distinguished journalism led him to establish the Columbia University School of Journalism and the annual Pulitzer Prizes "for the encouragement of public service, public morals, American Literature, and the advancement of education."

JULIUS ROSENWALD (1862-1932)

Born Springfield, Illinois; died Chicago, Illinois. Merchant and philanthropist.
PLAQUE: *Cast zinc, 7¹³⁄₁₆″ x 5¼″, by I. Sors. FB 452.*

Julius Rosenwald spent one unsuccessful year as a merchant in New York, after which he returned to Chicago and established the clothing firm of Rosenwald and Weil. In 1895, on receipt of an order for 10,000 suits from Sears, Roebuck and Company, he foresaw a great future for the new mail-order house, invested in it, and fourteen years later became its president (1909-25). Rosenwald was not only a farsighted businessman but also one of America's most munificent philanthropists. He was deeply interested in furthering educational opportunities for the Negro. As a trustee of Tuskegee Institute (1912-32), he played a major role in establishing its position among the finest colleges of the United States. In 1917 he set up the Julius Rosenwald Fund for the general betterment of the American Negro's condition. Other of his beneficiaries included: Jewish war relief organizations; agricultural settlements in Palestine, the Crimea, and the Ukraine; the University of Chicago; and the Chicago Museum of Science and Industry. It has been estimated that Rosenwald gave more than $70,000,000 in his efforts to provide for increased educational facilities throughout the world.

[87]

Baron JAMES MAYER de ROTHSCHILD (1792-1868)

Born Frankfurt-am-Main, Germany; died Paris, France. Banker and philanthropist.
PLAQUE: *Cast bronze, diam. 5⅛″, by Hovell. FB 554.*

Baron James de Rothschild established the French branch of the renowned family of international bankers when he opened the firm of Rothschild Frères in Paris in 1812. He was consul general to Austria-Hungary in 1822 and from that post negotiated loans of the utmost importance to the French Government. Like all Rothschilds of his generation, he unhesitatingly made use of his position of power and importance to better the condition of his fellow Jews, securing the repeal of a number of antisemitic laws and giving a hospital as an asylum for aged Jews. A patron of the arts, he was particularly interested in the furtherance of Hebrew literature and in the success of Jewish artists.

NATHAN MAYER ROTHSCHILD (1777-1836)

Born Frankfurt-am-Main, Germany; died London, England. Banker.
MEDAL: *Cast bronze, diam. 2⅜″, by H. Hyams. FB 84.*

The true financial genius of the famous Rothschild family, Nathan Mayer Rothschild went to England in 1798 and six years later founded the banking house that bears his name. So daring and successful were his innovations that by 1810 he had no serious competition. Convinced of the possibility of defeating Napoleon, he helped to finance the Duke of Wellington's campaign after the depletion of the royal treasury and, in order to keep in constant contact with the continent, set up a carrier pigeon station on the coast. It was in this way that he was the first in England to know of the British victory at Waterloo. Although Rothschild had been the chief representative of the Allied powers in their loan arrangements, never had his position been so firmly secure as it was—and would remain—after his and his country's stunning success in the Napoleonic War.

DAVID SASSOON (1793-1864)

Born Baghdad, Mesopotamia; died Bombay, India. Merchant and Philanthropist.
PLAQUE: *Cast bronze, 4⁷⁄₁₆″ x 5⅝″, by Kormis. FB 735.*

David Sassoon was educated in the Jewish tradition and trained in business. As early as 1829 he became the leader of the Baghdad Jewish community but soon had to flee the city due to the hostility to Jews of the reigning pasha. Having moved to Bombay in 1833, Sassoon opened an export business, sending English textiles to Persia and Mesopotamia and selling native products to British traders. His business gradually spread to Central Asia, China, and Japan, with a monopoly of trade in Indian yarn, Lancashire cottons, and opium. Although Sassoon spoke several oriental languages, he never learned English; when he became an English subject in 1853, he signed his name in Hebrew. He employed only Jews, building schools and synagogues for their benefit. Sassoon established many communal institutions in Bombay. When he died, his fortune was estimated at five million pounds.

DAVID SASSOON.

BORN BAGHDAD 1792

DIED BOMBAY 1864.

KORHIS

JACOB HENRY SCHIFF (1847-1920)

Born Frankfurt-am-Main, Germany; died New York City. Financier and philanthropist.

PLAQUE: *Cast bronze, 5¹³⁄₁₆″ x 3¹³⁄₁₆″, by I. Sors. FB 786.*

Jacob Schiff, born to a distinguished German Jewish family, was apprenticed to a business firm in 1861. He came to America four years later but, failing in the brokerage business, returned to Germany in 1872. Kuhn, Loeb and Company brought him back to New York, however, and so acute was his knowledge of finance that in 1888 he was made head of the firm. Schiff was one of the most brilliant financiers of his day, playing a leading role in the development of the American railroads. As a philanthropist he promoted the Tuskegee Institute and other Negro educational institutions, was a founder of the American Jewish Committee, treasurer of the New York chapter of Red Cross for many years, and president and guiding light of Montefiore Hospital. He also established the departments of semitic languages at the New York Public Library and the Library of Congress and gave the funds for the first Jewish Publication Society translation of the Bible. Schiff not only donated vast sums of money, but also gave unsparingly of his own time and energy in his efforts to improve the lot of mankind.

NATHAN STRAUS (1848-1931)

Born Otterberg, Germany; died New York City. Merchant and philanthropist.

PLAQUE: *Cast bronze, 5¼″ x 4¾″, by A. Eisenberg. FB 422.*

Brought to America in 1854, Nathan Straus attended business school in New York City and afterward joined his father in the import business. In 1874 he became a partner in R. H. Macy & Company and by 1888 was co-owner with his brother Isidor. Four years later the brothers expanded their enterprise to include Abraham & Straus in Brooklyn. But it is as a philanthropist that Straus is best remembered. Interested primarily in immediate, practical aid for the needy, he originated and maintained a system of milk distribution for the poor of New York City (1890-1920), as well as coal depots and four houses where free bed and breakfast were provided. During the winter of 1914-15 alone, he provided 1,135,731 meals to be sold for a penny. In 1912 he established soup kitchens in Jerusalem and later was the chief donor of food for Palestinian war sufferers. Straus was the sole American delegate to the International Congress for Protection of Infants (Berlin, 1911) and to the Tuberculosis Congress (Rome, 1912).

JUDAH TOURO (1775-1854)

Born Newport, Rhode Island; died New Orleans, Louisiana. Merchant and philanthropist.

PLAQUE: *Cast bronze, 5⅞" x 4¾", by I. Sors. FB 548.*

In 1801 Judah Touro relinquished a job in his uncle's shipping business in Boston and moved to New Orleans. He established a general merchandise store there and soon became the owner of a number of ships and a considerable amount of real estate. Later devoting himself to philanthropy he established the Touro Free Library in New Orleans (1830), gave $10,000 toward the completion of Boston's Bunker Hill Monument (1843), and built a synagogue for New Orleans' Sephardic congregation (1850). Two years later he converted into a hospital an estate he had bought and donated it to the city in his will. Touro bequeathed almost the entirety of his fortune to charity, the majority going to nonsectarian institutions in New England, Jewish congregations in nineteen cities, Jewish benevolent societies, Jewish educational institutions, and various worthy causes in Palestine. He also gave substantial sums to Mt. Sinai Hospital in New York and toward the building of a park and library in his native city.

FELIX MORITZ WARBURG (1871-1937)

Born Hamburg, Germany; died New York City. Financier and philanthropist.
PLAQUE: *Cast bronze, 7" x 5", by I. Sors. FB 729.*

Felix Warburg came to America in 1894 and went to work for the firm of Kuhn, Loeb and Company. Although senior partner at the time of his death, Warburg's interests were directed far less toward finance than toward philanthropy. Appointed to the New York City Board of Education in 1902, he promoted special schools for retarded children and the placement of blind children in regular classes so that they might be prepared to live normal lives. He demanded thorough education for immigrants and was concerned with all types of social work. An advocate of juvenile courts, Warburg was a member of the first New York State Probation Commission (1907). He also helped to found the Federation for the Support of Jewish Philanthropic Societies, which aids in the collection and disbursement of funds for Jewish charities, and was its president (1917-20) and chairman of the board (1925-37).

OSKAR WASSERMANN (1869-1934)

Born Bamberg, Germany; died Garmisch, Germany. Banker.
PLAQUE: *Cast bronze, diam. 4⅛", by I. Sors. FB 800.*

Oskar Wassermann entered his family's banking firm (founded 1785) as a young man and soon became a director of A. E. Wassermann in Berlin. He was one of Germany's most respected financiers and a director of the Deutsche Bank (1912-33), but he was forced to resign that post when the Nazis began their all-out attack on German Jewry in 1933. Wassermann, a non-Zionist, was nonetheless a leader in reconstruction work for Palestine. As president of the German branch of Keren Hayesod (Palestine Foundation Fund) and a member of the board of directors of the world organization, he assisted primarily in the raising and sensible allocation of funds for Palestinian relief. Although Wassermann was one of the least heralded workers for the rebirth of Palestine, he played a large part in fashioning a positive German Jewish attitude toward the revitalization of the Holy Land.

Science
&
Medicine

GREAT JEWISH PORTRAITS IN METAL

ALFRED ADLER (1870-1937)

Born Vienna, Austria; died Aberdeen, Scotland. Psychologist.
PLAQUE: *Cast bronze, 6 5/16" x 5", by I. Sors. FB 461.*

Alfred Adler studied with Sigmund Freud from 1902 until 1911, when he left him due to irreconcilable differences between them respecting theory. Adler accepted Freud's determinism but believed that organic inferiority rather than unconscious psychological drives determines man's behavior. He stressed the importance of a sense of inferiority (especially, organ inferiority) and asserted that man's striving for superiority (his desire for self-assertion) is the dominant factor in his behavior pattern. Adler was the founder of the school of Individual Psychology, which holds that all individuals are unique and, as a result, interpret situations differently and have different opinions of themselves and of their worlds. Having gained wide acceptance in the United States, Adler settled in America in 1935. He was the author of *The Practice and Theory of Individual Psychology* (1920), *Problems of Neurosis* (1929), and *Social Unrest* (1933).

HIPPOLYTE BERNHEIM (1840-1919)

Born Mulhouse, France; died Paris, France. Psychologist.
PLAQUE: *Cast bronze, 2 11/16" x 3 9/16", by V. Rouvé. FB 16.*

After receiving his M.D. from the University of Strasbourg in 1867, Hippolyte Bernheim served on the faculty there until 1871. Transferring to Nancy, in 1878 he became professor of the medical clinic and within two years had established the school of psychology known as the "school of Nancy." An advocate of hypnotism as invaluable to the new field of psychotherapy, Bernheim found his thesis both applauded and, more often, mocked. He did, however, have the satisfaction of achieving a certain success in the use of his methods of therapy. Among the works that he wrote in explanation and defense of his theories were *Concerning Suggestion in the Hypnotic and Waking States* (1884), *Concerning Suggestion and Its Application to Therapeutics* (1887), and *Hypnosis, Suggestion, and Psychotherapy* (1890).

FRANZ BOAS (1858-1942)

Born Minden, Germany; died New York City. Anthropologist.
PLAQUE: *Cast bronze, 5 11/16" x 5 3/16", by I. Sors. FB 458.*

Franz Boas studied at Heidelberg, Bonn, and Kiel. He became interested in anthropology only after observing the Eskimos while on a meteorological expedition to Baffin Island. Appointed instructor at the University of Berlin and assistant at the Royal Ethnographical Museum in 1885, he traveled to the Canadian Pacific coast to investigate Indian tribes. This resulted in his now classic theory of the cultural relationship between Eskimos, American Indians, and Siberians. As professor of anthropology at Columbia University (1899-1937) Boas studied the effects of environment on human physiology and mentality. In *The Mind of Primitive Man* (1911) he propounded the theory that there is no difference in the thought processes of primitive and civilized men, thus dealing the first scientific blow to the concept of racial superiority. A dedicated antiracist, Boas fought the "Hun theory" during World War I and "Aryanism" during the 1930's. Among his best known books are *Anthropology and Modern Life* (1928) and *Race, Language, and Culture* (1940).

V. Rouvé

au Professeur Bernheim
ses Collègues, ses élèves, ses Amis   1910

ABRAHAM ARDEN BRILL (1874-1948)

Born Kanczuga, Austria; died New York City. Psychoanalyst.
PLAQUE: *Cast bronze, 6⅜″ x 4⅞″, by I. Sors. FB 636.*

A. A. Brill was graduated from New York University in 1901 and received his medical degree from Columbia University two years later. After continuing his studies at the Psychiatric Clinic in Zürich, Switzerland, he returned to America in 1908 and spent the next few years working as a psychiatrist in several clinics. Brill lectured on psychoanalysis at New York University and at Columbia University, where he helped to introduce the Freudian school of psychoanalysis in America. He wrote extensively on that subject and also translated the principal works of Freud and Jung into English. With Ernest Jones, he was a founder of the American Psychoanalytic Society and served as its president for many years. Brill's writings include *Psychoanalysis: Its Theories and Applications* (1914) and *Fundamental Conceptions of Psychoanalysis* (1922).

GEORG FERDINAND CANTOR (1845-1918)

Born St. Petersburg, Russia; died Halle, Germany. Mathematician.
PLAQUE: *Cast bronze, 6½″ x 4⅛″, by C. S. Paolo. FB 747.*

Georg Cantor received his doctorate from the University of Berlin in 1867. As professor at the University of Halle, he began his investigation into the Fourier series of trigonometric functions. This resulted in his now classic theory of irrational numbers. Later Cantor developed an arithmetic of the infinite and an entirely new branch of mathematics, the theory of sets of points. Although the subject of learned dispute at the time, his theories have not only been generally accepted, but have also had a profound influence on twentieth-century mathematics. His *Contributions to the Founding of the Theory of Transfinite Numbers* (1915) is a standard work in the field.

MORITZ BENEDIKT CANTOR (1829-1920)

Born Mannheim, Germany; died Heidelberg, Germany. Mathematician.
PLAQUE: *Cast bronze, 4¹⁵⁄₁₆″ x 4⅛″, by I. Sors. FB 795.*

After studies at the University of Göttingen, Moritz Cantor received his Ph.D. from the University of Heidelberg (1851), where two years later he joined the faculty. His interest and extraordinary ability in both history and mathematics led him to write his monumental, three-volume *Lectures on the History of Mathematics* (1880-98), of which a fourth volume was prepared by nine scholars working under his supervision. With this complete and authoritative work Cantor established the field of history of the exact sciences. He founded the *Critical Journal of Chemistry, Mathematics, and Physics.* Cantor was also founder and editor (1859-1901) of the *Journal of Mathematics and Physics.*

PAUL EHRLICH (1854-1915)

Born Strehlen, Germany; died Hamburg, Germany. Immunologist.
MEDAL: *Cast bronze, diam. 2⅜″, by Goetz. FB 20.*

As a medical student, Paul Ehrlich became interested in chemistry and bacteriological research. He was named director of the Institute for Experimental Therapy at Frankfurt-am-Main in 1899 and professor at the University of Frankfurt fifteen years later. By discovering the existence of antibodies, Ehrlich established the doctrine of immunobiological relations and founded the vitally important science of hematology. He also created a new branch of chemotherapy with the introduction of Salvarsan (1910) in the treatment of syphilis, thus marking a new era in the long history of struggle against that disease. In 1908 Ehrlich shared the Nobel Prize for medicine. His monumental work dominated the thought of an entire generation in the field of immunology, where many future advances were due directly to his investigations and discoveries.

ALBERT EINSTEIN (1879-1955)

Born Ulm, Germany; died Princeton, New Jersey. Theoretical physicist.
PLAQUE: *Cast bronze, diam. 5⅞", by A. Eisenberg. FB 613.*

Albert Einstein received his doctorate from the University of Zürich in 1905 and soon became one of the greatest scientists of the twentieth century. After teaching theoretical physics at Zürich and Prague, he was named director of the Kaiser Wilhelm Academy of Science in Berlin (1914-33). While there he developed his theory of relativity, explained Brownian movement, demonstrated the quantum theory of matter, and did extensive study in the thermal properties of light. He was awarded the 1921 Nobel Prize for his unequalled contributions to theoretical physics. Fleeing Germany in 1933, he came to America where, until his death, he was associated with the Institute for Advanced Study at Princeton. Although for us his name is synonymous with genius, Einstein was a man of surpassing humility and gentleness whose great scientific knowledge only increased his deep personal religious convictions and humanitarianism.

SIMON FLEXNER (1863-1946)

Born Louisville, Kentucky; died New York City. Bacteriologist and pathologist.
PLAQUE: *Cast bronze. 5¹/₁₆″ x 3½″, by I. Sors. FB 476.*

Brother of the famed educator Abraham Flexner, Simon Flexner received his medical degree from the University of Louisville in 1889, after which he did postgraduate work both in this country and abroad. He was professor of pathological anatomy at Johns Hopkins University (1898-99) and of pathology at the University of Pennsylvania (1899-1903). From 1903 to 1935 he was director of laboratories for the Rockefeller Institute for Medical Research (director of the Institute, 1920-35). An authority on poisons, particularly on the biochemical constitution of snake venoms, Flexner also discovered the cause of dysentery and the virus that causes poliomyelitis and developed a curative serum for the treatment of spinal meningitis. He was a member of the National Advisory Health Council and joint editor of the *Rockefeller Institute Journal of Experimental Medicine*. Flexner wrote more than three hundred and fifty articles on medical subjects and was the recipient of numerous honorary Sc.D.'s.

SIGMUND FREUD (1856-1939)

Born Freiberg, Austria; died London, England. Originator of psychoanalysis.
MEDAL: *Cast bronze, diam. 2⅜″, by C. M. Schwerdtner, Jr. FB 14.*

Graduated from the medical school of the University of Vienna, Sigmund Freud soon became interested in hypnosis. At first a general practitioner, he began gradually to emphasize neuropathology and by 1895 had developed the investigative technique known as "free association." As the field of psychoanalysis became more and more a reality, Freud announced his revolutionary theories in such works as *The Interpretation of Dreams* (1900) and *Totem and Taboo* (1913). Bitter controversy surrounded his contention that neuroses are due to conflicts in the unconscious mind and that most of these conflicts are traceable to infantile sexuality. His last book, *Moses and Monotheism* (1939), provoked as great a storm of disapproval as had his first, even though the interval had brought general acceptance of his basic theories. It would be impossible to calculate the immensity of Freud's contributions to the understanding of human behavior or of his impact on our lives in the twentieth century.

FRITZ HABER (1868-1934)

Born Breslau, Germany; died Basel, Switzerland. Physical chemist.
PLAQUE: *Cast bronze, diam. 5⁹⁄₁₆″, by I. Sors. FB 669.*

Fritz Haber was a professor at the University of Berlin when in 1911 he was appointed to the directorship of the Kaiser Wilhelm Institute for physical chemistry and electrochemistry. It was while there that he was instrumental in the discovery of a method of producing ammonia from atmospheric nitrogen. This technique, the "Haber process," was of great importance to Germany during World War I, at which time Haber organized the German chemical war industry. In 1918 he received the Nobel Prize for chemistry. Although he had converted to Christianity in 1906, he was dismissed from his post in 1933 due to his outspoken resentment against the Nazis for firing his Jewish assistants. He spent the last year of his life in voluntary exile in Switzerland.

HEINRICH HERTZ (1857-1894)

Born Hamburg, Germany; died Bonn, Germany. Physicist.
PLAQUE: *Cast bronze, 5¹⁄₁₆″ x 3¹¹⁄₁₆″, by I. Sors. FB 784.*

A student of Helmholtz, Heinrich Hertz was lecturer in physics at the University of Kiel (1883-85), professor at Karlsruhe Polytechnic (1885-89), and professor at the University of Bonn (1889-94). Working in electromagnetism, he discovered the correspondence between electromagnetic waves and light waves, thus proving the electromagnetic nature of light itself. This discovery led directly to the inventions of wireless telegraphy and radio. His studies in the field of light had brought him close to the discovery of the x-ray, but death at the age of thirty-six prevented his adding that to his list of phenomenal accomplishments. While at Bonn he did research on the discharge of electricity in rarefied gases and produced his brilliant treatise on the *Principles of Mechanics*.

CESARE LOMBROSO (1835-1909)

Born Verona, Italy; died Turin, Italy. Psychiatrist and criminologist.
PLAQUE: *Cast bronze, diam. 4⅛″, by I. Sors. FB 690.*

Cesare Lombroso studied medicine in Italy and Austria. In 1862 he accepted a position as lecturer in psychiatry at the University of Pavia, where he devoted himself to criminology. Lombroso believed in "born criminals" and advanced the theory that criminality is due to the survival of primitive physical and psychological traits in man. He discovered that physical, nervous, and mental abnormalities appeared more often in criminals than in noncriminals and credited this in part to atavism and in part to degeneration. Greatly influenced by positivism, he felt that all mental phenomena were due to biological causes. Lombroso was the author of many controversial books on criminology and in 1894 published a treatise in which he attributed antisemitism to hereditary primitivism. He was at one time an Italian national hero, but all monuments erected in his honor were destroyed during the Fascist regime, and the numerous streets that once had been Via Lombroso were renamed.

JONAS EDWARD SALK (1914-)

Born New York City. Epidemiologist and physician.
PLAQUE: *Cast bronze, diam. 6¹⁄₁₆″, by A. P. d'Andrea. FB 1098.*

Jonas Salk received his B.S. from the City College of New York in 1934 and his M.D. from New York University five years later. He did important research on influenza vaccines and in 1949 became professor of bacteriology at the University of Pittsburgh and head of its department of preventive medicine in 1954. In the latter year he became known throughout the world for his discovery of a preventive vaccine for poliomyelitis. Since 1957 Salk has been professor of experimental medicine at the University of Pittsburgh. A brilliant virologist, he is one of the truly great scientists of our time and is the recipient of many honorary degrees. In 1962 dedication ceremonies were held for the Salk Institute for Biological Studies, which opened in La Jolla, California, in 1963 with Dr. Salk as director.

BÉLA SCHICK (1877-)

Born Boglár, Hungary. Pediatrician.
PLAQUE: *Cast bronze, 6″ x 4½″, by I. Sors. FB 462.*

Béla Schick received his M.D. from the Karl Franz University in Graz, Austria, and two years later began the practice of medicine in Vienna. Beginning in 1902 he taught at the University, eventually serving as professor of pediatrics (1918-23). Schick is best known for his discovery of a method for determining susceptibility to diphtheria (1913), but he has also done important work on tuberculosis, scarlet fever, and the nutrition of newborn infants. He came to America in 1923, was clinical professor of children's diseases at Columbia University (1936-43), and has acted as adviser and director of numerous pediatrics departments in New York City. Author of numerous articles and books, Schick was also co-author of *Serum Krankheit* (1905), *Scarlet Fever* (1912), and *Child Care Today* (1933).

JACOB da SILVA SOLIS-COHEN (1838-1927)

Born New York City; died Philadelphia, Pennsylvania. Laryngologist and surgeon.
PLAQUE: *Cast bronze, 5⁵⁄₁₆″ x 3⁹⁄₁₆″, by Mantel. FB 566.*

Jacob da Silva Solis-Cohen received his medical degree from the University of Pennsylvania in 1860. He immediately enlisted in the Union Army and was appointed assistant surgeon in the 26th Regiment, Pennsylvania Volunteers. Transferred later to the Navy, he was at one time acting fleet surgeon to the South Atlantic Blockading Squadron. After the war he began his investigations into the new science of laryngology. His findings were published in numerous treatises and brought him immediate fame in medical circles. Solis-Cohen was founder and editor of the *Archives of Laryngology* and editor of the department of laryngology of the *American Journal of Medical Sciences*. He helped to found the Conference of American Physicians and Surgeons, the American Laryngologic Association (of which he was president, 1880-82), and the Philadelphia Polyclinic, where he was the first professor of diseases of the chest and throat. Solis-Cohen is known as the "father of laryngology."

[101]

AUGUST von WASSERMANN (1866-1925)

Born Bamberg, Germany; died Berlin, Germany. Immunologist and diagnostician.

PLAQUE: *Cast bronze, 6½″ x 5⅛″, by I. Sors. FB 115.*

August von Wassermann was educated in Germany and in 1888 began the practice of medicine in Strasbourg. In 1906, after years of research, he gained international renown for his discovery of serodiagnosis for syphilis—the famous Wassermann reaction, by which past infection and present activity of the disease can be established. Thereafter he lived in Berlin as director of the department of experimental therapy and serum research at the Robert Koch Institute for Infectious Diseases and as director of the Kaiser Wilhelm Institute. Wassermann helped to develop an antitoxin for diphtheria and preventive serums for typhoid, cholera, and tetanus. He was the author of numerous studies, of which the best known are included in the *Handbook of Pathological Microorganisms* (1902-09).

Arts
&
Literature

GREAT JEWISH PORTRAITS IN METAL

MARK MATVEEVICH ANTOKOLSKI (1843-1902)

Born Vilna, Lithuania; died Hamburg, Germany. Sculptor.
PLAQUE: *Cast bronze, 5″ x 3¹¹⁄₁₅″, by I. Sors. FB 621.*

Mark Antokolski entered the St. Petersburg Academy of Fine Arts in 1863 and within two years had so distinguished himself that he was granted a scholarship to study in Berlin. A devoted student of Russian history, in 1871 Antokolski produced his *Ivan the Terrible* and overnight became one of the best known sculptors in the world. He was an uncompromising realist whose work was noted for its meticulous detail and for its serious dedication to the search for the meaning behind form. Never content with portraiture or with an analytic treatment of figures themselves, Antokolski essayed the depiction of the thoughts and emotions of the men he portrayed. Among his works are *Peter I* (1872), *The Head of John the Baptist* (1878), and *Spinoza* (1882). The first great Jewish sculptor, Antokolski overcame deep-rooted family objections to his art and proved to be one of the most important artists of the nineteenth century.

SHOLEM ASCH (1880-1957)

Born Kutno, Poland; died London, England. Novelist and playwright.
PLAQUE: *Cast bronze, 5³⁄₁₆″ x 3⅞″, by M. Newman. FB 515.*

Sholem Asch was the most widely read Yiddish writer of his time, having achieved popularity through various literary forms. An idyllic novel *The Town* won him early public notice, and his drama *The God of Vengeance* was produced in Berlin in 1910 by Max Reinhardt, subsequently being presented all over the world. Several of his later plays were outstandingly successful in the Yiddish theatre of New York City. His novels, *The Nazarene* (1939), *The Apostle* (1943), *East River* (1946), *Mary* (1949), and *Moses* (1951), attempted to bring Christians and Jews closer together by pointing out their common spiritual heritage. Asch's point of view incurred severe criticism from both Jews and Christians, but his artistry overcame any adverse public opinion and earned for him an unparalleled position among Yiddish writers of the twentieth century.

BERTHOLD AUERBACH (1812-1882)

Born Nordstetten, Germany; died Cannes, France. Writer.
PLAQUE: *Cast bronze, 5¼″ x 4⅜″, by Mantel. FB 610.*

Educated at the University of Tübingen, Berthold Auerbach chose
not to pursue the rabbinical career asked of him by his parents but
turned instead to literary scholarship and writing. Greatly influenced
by Spinoza, he published a biography of that great philosopher and
a five-volume edition of his works (1841). It was not until the publication of his *Tales of the Black Forest* (1843-61), however, that
he became famous throughout Germany. These simple stories of
German peasant life, delicately superimposed upon an underlying
current of philosophical reflection, were a high point in the history
of German literary romanticism. Among Auerbach's other works are
The Barefoot One (1856), *Edelweiss* (1861), and numerous articles
and pamphlets on antisemitism.

LÉON BAKST (1868-1924)

Born St. Petersburg, Russia; died Paris, France. Painter.
PLAQUE: *Cast bronze, 4⅞″ x 3¹³⁄₁₆″, by I. Sors. FB 799.*

Raised in St. Petersburg, Léon Bakst attended the Imperial Academy
of Arts and soon gained great success as a court painter. His truly
important work did not begin until 1900, however, when he assumed
the position of scenic artist for the Hermitage Court and Imperial
Theatres. He revolutionized theatrical set designing by his insistence
that sets and costumes be an integral part of the drama and not an
irrelevant form of self-expression for the artist. As designer for Sergei
Diaghilev's productions of the ballets *Cleopatra, Scheherazade, The
Firebird, Daphnis and Chloë,* and *Afternoon of a Faun* he showed himself to be the first truly intelligent and able set designer of modern
times. A neo-romantic, Bakst synthesized Eastern and Western art
and had a lasting influence on scenic design throughout the Western
world. He is known today as one of the greatest of modern Russian
artists.

TRISTAN BERNARD (1866-1947)

Born Besançon, France; died Paris, France. Playwright and novelist.
PLAQUE: *Cast bronze, 5¼" x 3⁹⁄₁₆", by I. Sors. FB 575.*

Tristan Bernard began his literary career by writing short stories and sketches for magazines. He later turned to drama and, after producing a number of highly successful one-act comedies, entered the field of vaudeville, where his *Unknown Dancer* (1907) and *The Little Café* (1911) were spectacular hits of their day. His best works, however, appeared immediately before and during World War I, when he devoted himself to brilliant, satirical exposés of human weakness. His biting wit and irony were best displayed in *Prince Charming* (1914) and *Man's Will* (1917). After the war, he returned to vaudeville, where his merciless observations and brilliant dialogue brought him continued success in such works as *The Prodigal Child of Vésinet* (1921), *The Unforeseen Voyage* (1928), and *Nocturnal Visits* (1935).

HENRI LÉON GUSTAVE CHARLES BERNSTEIN (1875-1953)

Born and died Paris, France. Playwright.
PLAQUE: *Cast bronze, 5⅜" x 3⅞", by I. Sors. FB 630.*

Henri Bernstein was educated at the Universities of Paris and Cambridge. A man of brilliant intellect and great talent, with an uncanny ability to make familiar plots appear fresh and new, Bernstein made his playwriting debut with *Le Marché* in 1900. From 1900 to 1914 he wrote light comedies, but with the start of World War I his plays generally concentrated upon political oppression and the restlessness and confusion of the individual in the twentieth century. Bernstein fled to the United States after the fall of Paris in 1940 but returned to his homeland at the end of the war. Among his many works are *The Assault* (1912), *The Secret* (1913), *Judith* (1922), *Felix* (1926), and *Elvire* (1940).

CHAIM NACHMAN BIALIK (1873-1934)

Born Radi, Russia; died Vienna, Austria. Poet and scholar.
PLAQUE: *Cast bronze, 6⁹⁄₁₆" x 4¹⁵⁄₁₆", by I. Sors. FB 34.*

Chaim Nachman Bialik was raised by his grandfather, who instilled in him a love of Hebrew literature. He met Ahad Ha-am in Odessa and began to contribute poems to his publication *Hashiloach*. The poem that brought him fame, "In the City of Slaughter," was inspired by the Kishineff pogrom of Easter 1903. This poem, along with other of Bialik's works of this period, gave added impetus to the self-defense and Zionist movements among the Jews in Eastern Europe. Bialik settled in Palestine in 1924, re-establishing there the publishing house, Dvir, which he had founded in Odessa. It was Bialik, the poet laureate of the Jewish renaissance, who demonstrated the true depth and expressiveness of the modern Hebrew language. Among his most famous poems are "The Desert Dead," "Aftergrowth," and "The Scroll of Fire." He also translated into Hebrew a large number of literary classics, including *Don Quixote, Wilhelm Tell,* and many of Shakespeare's works.

GEORG MORRIS COHEN BRANDES (1842-1927)

Born and died Copenhagen, Denmark. Writer and literary critic.
PLAQUE: *Cast bronze, 2¾″ x 3⁹/₁₆″, by Kormis. FB 635.*

After graduation from the University of Copenhagen (1859), Georg Brandes quickly established himself as a revolutionary critic and thinker. He demanded that the author seek truth and insisted that this truth (science and philosophy) could never live side by side with orthodoxy. He condemned Danish literature as childish and, soon finding himself unwelcome in his native land, went to Berlin in 1877. Five years later he returned, however, an internationally respected critic. His final triumph came in 1902 with his elevation to the professorship of aesthetics at the University of Copenhagen. His best known work is the collection of his lectures published as *Main Currents in Nineteenth-Century Literature* (1872-90), but he also wrote highly perceptive works on *Disraeli* (1878), *Ferdinand Lassalle* (1881), *Shakespeare* (1895-96), *Nietzsche* (1909), and *Goethe* (1915). Brandes was the first truly scientific student of literature and had an incalculable influence on twentieth-century literary criticism, of which, indeed, he is the father.

MAX BROD (1884-   )

Born Prague, Bohemia. Writer.
PLAQUE: *Cast bronze, 5⅜″ x 5⅛″, by I. Sors. FB 872.*

Max Brod became sympathetic to the Zionist cause shortly before World War I. He was later one of the founders of the Jewish National Council of Prague (1918) and served as its vice-president. Shortly before Nazi troops invaded Czechoslovakia in 1939, Brod settled in Palestine, where he became a dramatist for the Habima Theatre in Tel Aviv. A prolific writer of fiction, poetry, and essays, and a contributor to numerous Hebrew periodicals, Brod displays in his work a preoccupation with the problem of evil and the idea of collective responsibility. Among his works are *Tycho Brahe's Redemption* (1916) and *Reubeni, Prince of the Jews* (1925), as well as a collection of essays, *Socialism in Zionism* (1920). Brod has also written biographies of Adolph Schreiber (1921), of Leos Janacek (1925), and of his friend Franz Kafka (1927), whose work he edited.

MARC CHAGALL (1887-   )

Born Vitebsk, Russia. Painter.
PLAQUE: *Cast bronze, diam. 6¼″, by E. Quattrocchi. FB 1089.*

Refused by the Imperial Academy of Fine Arts in 1907, Marc Chagall studied in St. Petersburg under Léon Bakst who, although he rejected the young artist's set designs as too outlandish, took him to Paris in 1910. Chagall, attracted to, though not confined by, cubism, soon began the work that has made him world-famous. From 1914 to 1923 Chagall was back in Vitebsk, where he founded an art school and museum and produced scenic designs for the early Soviet theatre. Returning to Paris, he did his brilliant illustrations for editions of Gogol's *Dead Souls*, La Fontaine's *Fables,* and the Bible and continued the exuberant, mystic works that are his trademark. In America (1941-48) he once again gained particular success with his set designs. Chagall's twelve stained glass windows for the chapel of the Hadassah—Hebrew University Medical Center (1961) were among the most widely discussed works in modern art history.

Sir JACOB EPSTEIN (1880-1959)

Born New York City; died London, England. Sculptor.

PLAQUE: *Cast bronze, 7¼" x 5⁷⁄₁₆", by A. Eisenberg. FB 608.*

Sir Jacob Epstein was born and raised on New York's Lower East Side and was educated at the Art Students' League and at the École des Beaux Arts in Paris. In 1905 he went to London and two years later was commissioned to execute eighteen figures for the British Medical Association building. From that time forward controversy surrounded his work, the primitive power and simplicity of which were startling long after he had been acknowledged as one of the foremost sculptors of the twentieth century. Epstein, equally adept in many media, created sculpture encompassing a wide range of subjects. Among his most famous works are *Two Doves* (1913), *Day and Night* (1929), *Genesis* (1931), and *Adam* (1939). Particularly noteworthy among his busts are those of Joseph Conrad (1924), Albert Einstein (1933), and George Bernard Shaw (1934). Epstein was knighted by King George VI in 1954.

LYONEL CHARLES ADRIAN FEININGER (1871-1956)

Born and died New York City. Painter.

PLAQUE: *Cast bronze, diam. 4", by Simpson. FB 48.*

Lyonel Feininger was educated in art schools in Hamburg, Berlin, and Paris. Known first for his caricatures and illustrations in German and Parisian weeklies (1893-1907), Feininger turned to serious painting in 1907. By 1913 he was one of the famous "Blue Rider" group that revolutionized German painting in the second decade of the twentieth century. An instructor in painting and graphic arts at the internationally known Bauhaus (Weimar, 1919-25; Dessau, 1925-32), Feininger characterized his work as being paintings not of objects, but of the space around objects. Among his best known works are *Side-Wheeler* (1913), *Locomotive with the Big Wheel* (1915), *Village Church* (1924), and *Gables I* (1925). After his return to America in 1933, Feininger did his famous murals for the New York World's Fair (1940) and many other works that may be found today in museums throughout the United States.

EDNA FERBER (1887-   )

Born Kalamazoo, Michigan. Novelist.

PLAQUE: *Cast bronze, 5⅝" x 3¹⁵⁄₁₆", by I. Sors. FB 475.*

Raised in Wisconsin, Edna Ferber became a reporter for the *Appleton Daily Crescent* at the age of seventeen. After jobs with the *Milwaukee Journal* and the *Chicago Tribune*, Miss Ferber began devoting all of her time to the novels that made her famous. Noted for their wide range of locale and subject matter, they include *So Big* (Pulitzer Prize, 1924), the story of a widow on a tractor farm in Illinois; *Show Boat* (1926), a narrative of the Mississippi; *Cimarron* (1929), the migration to Western America; *Come and Get It* (1935), a tale of Wisconsin lumbermen; and *Giant* (1952), the rise of a Texas rancher. She also collaborated with the late George S. Kaufman on a number of highly successful plays: *The Royal Family* (1928) and *Dinner at Eight* (1932), among others. Miss Ferber may well be the most consistently popular novelist America has ever known, having written best sellers for three generations of readers.

LION FEUCHTWANGER (1884-1958)

Born Munich, Germany; died Los Angeles, California. Novelist and playwright.
PLAQUE: *Cast bronze, 6" x 4½", by I. Sors. FB 472.*

Lion Feuchtwanger was educated in Munich, where he studied philosophy and literature under many leading scholars. Inspired by them, he wrote a number of brilliant and provocative critical articles during the period 1905-10. Shortly thereafter he achieved success in the drama, and in 1925 his novel *Jud Süss* was greeted with international acclaim. *Success* (1930), Feuchtwanger's first contemporary novel, was attacked in Germany for its unfriendly and ill-disguised depiction of certain Nazi high officials. Subsequently blacklisted by Hitler, he was expelled in 1933 and sought refuge in France. When it, too, was occupied by the Nazis, he escaped to Lisbon and, with the aid of friends, contrived to flee to the United States, where he spent the remaining years of his life. Among his major works are *The Ugly Duckling* (1923) and *Josephus* (1932-42), an historical trilogy.

HEINRICH HEINE (1797-1856)

Born Düsseldorf, Germany; died Paris, France. Poet and essayist.
MEDAL: *Struck silver, diam. 2", artist unknown. FB 40N.*

After years of restless travel and study, Heinrich Heine was graduated from the University of Göttingen in 1825. The next year a volume of poetry, *Die Harzreise*, appeared and was followed in 1827 by *Buch der Lieder*, one of the most beautiful volumes of lyric poetry ever written. In 1831 Heine, hailing the French Revolution of 1830, left Germany for Paris. He remained there until his death. His satiric essays, among the most brilliant ever written, attacked the German social system, and soon the German authorities took steps to censor his books and to restrict their sale. As a result of these measures Heine found his income severely curtailed and had to live for many years on a pension from the French Government. Heine is best remembered for his romantic lyric poetry with its bold use of nature symbolism and for his daring expressions of sympathy with all revolutionary causes.

HUGO von HOFMANNSTHAL (1874-1929)

Born and died Vienna, Austria. Poet, playwright, and librettist.
PLAQUE: *Cast bronze, 5⅚" x 3⅚", by I. Sors. FB 582.*

While still a student in Vienna, Hugo von Hofmannsthal became the originator of Austrian romanticism through his lyric and semi-dramatic poetry. He soon entered the field of the drama, where his extraordinary love and understanding of the ancients brought him great acclaim. Second only to Lorenzo Da Ponte as a librettist, he is best known to us today for the superb libretti written for the operas of his friend Richard Strauss: *Elektra* (1903), *Der Rosenkavalier* (1911), *Ariadne auf Naxos* (1912), and *Die Frau ohne Schatten* (1919). Constantly striving for formal perfection, Hofmannsthal recognized the unsurpassability of the classics, and many of his finest works were adaptations. His version of *Everyman* (1911), for example, was produced annually by Max Reinhardt at the Salzburg Festival. His collected poetry was published in 1911.

JOSEF ISRAËLS (1824-1911)

Born Groningen, Holland; died The Hague, Holland. Painter.
PLAQUE: *Cast bronze, 7⅛″ x 4⅞″, by I. Sors. FB 247.*

Having studied under several famous painters of the romantic school, Josef Israëls attempted to adopt their style. He gained no recognition in this way, however, and decided to portray the common people of his country. He painted fishermen, peasants, and laborers with such depth of sympathy and understanding that he soon became the most popular artist in all of Holland. Nor were his fellow Jews absent from his canvas. Well-trained in Talmud as a child, he was deeply moved by the European persecution of the Jews and expressed his emotions in a number of very realistic and powerful works with Jewish subjects. Israëls was one of the greatest Dutch painters of the nineteenth century and the recipient of many medals. Today no less than thirty of his paintings hang in the Rijksmuseum in Amsterdam, with many others throughout Europe and the United States.

EMMA LAZARUS (1849-1887)

Born and died New York City. Poet and essayist.
PLAQUE: *Cast bronze, 4⅛″ x 4¹⁵⁄₁₆″, by Mantel. FB 433.*

Although she was of Sephardic lineage, Emma Lazarus did not profess an interest in Judaism until a few years before her death. She was already a well-known and greatly admired poetess when she visited Ward's Island and saw the victims of the czarist persecutions of 1880-81. This experience led her to become an ardent proponent not only of Judaism, but also of Zionism. In 1882 Miss Lazarus wrote an article for *Century Magazine* entitled "Russian Christianity versus Modern Judaism." She also began the study of Hebrew and, with the aid of German translations, rendered medieval Judaeo-Spanish poetry into English. In 1874 she wrote *Alide*, a novel based on an episode in Goethe's life and, in 1881, published her translations of the poems and ballads of Heine. Miss Lazarus is best known, however, for her sonnet "The New Colossus," which is inscribed on the pedestal of the Statue of Liberty. These fourteen lines are perhaps the most succinct and beautiful statement of American principles ever written.

LUDWIG LEWISOHN (1883-1955)

Born Berlin, Germany; died Miami, Florida. Writer and educator.
PLAQUE: *Cast bronze, 5″ x 3⅞″, by I. Sors. FB 868.*

Ludwig Lewisohn was graduated from the College of Charleston (South Carolina) in 1901 and immediately embarked upon a career as a magazine writer. He taught for a year at the University of Wisconsin and was named professor of German language and literature at Ohio State University in 1911, later resigning that post to join the editorial staff of *The Nation* (1919-24). A lifelong Zionist and Zionist leader, Lewisohn served as editor of *The New Palestine* (1943-48) and was the author of numerous books on Jewish subjects. He was one of the most prolific twentieth-century writers and is best remembered for *Roman Summer* (1927), *The Island Within* (1928), *Stephen Escott* (1930), and the brilliant biography and critical study, *Goethe: The Story of a Man* (two volumes, 1949). Lewisohn, a highly successful novelist, was also a noted scholar and spent the last years of his life on the faculty of Brandeis University.

JOSEPH ISRAELS

1824
1911

MAX LIEBERMANN (1847-1935)

Born and died Berlin, Germany. Painter and etcher.
PLAQUE: *Cast bronze, 2⅞″ x 2⁹⁄₁₆″, by H. Kaufman. FB 50.*

After studying in Berlin, Max Liebermann went to Weimar (1869), Paris (1873), Munich (1878), and, every summer, to Holland. By the time he returned to Berlin in 1884 he had already painted many of the masterpieces that were to make him the most respected artist in the German capital. He was greatly influenced by Munkacsy and Israëls but nonetheless abjured sentimentality and all forms of novelty. Limiting himself to an objectivity tempered only by an uncommon sensitivity to the world around him, Liebermann was the undisputed leader of German impressionism. He was a professor at the Prussian Academy of Art after 1898 and its president (1920-28) and honorary president (1928-33). He was later denounced by the Nazis and spent the last two years of his life in retirement in Berlin—forbidden even to paint. A man of great wit and spontaneity, Liebermann was noted particularly for his portraits and his moving depictions of the day-to-day life of the Dutch Jews whom he so dearly loved.

EMIL LUDWIG (1881-1948)

Born Breslau, Germany; died Ascona, Switzerland. Biographer.
PLAQUE: *Cast bronze, 6⅛″ x 4½″, by I. Sors. FB 539.*

Emil Ludwig (né Cohn) first worked in the area of the drama but met with little success. As a result, he went to study in England where, during World War I, he was employed by a Berlin newspaper as foreign correspondent. It was at this time that he began work in the field of biography, soon gaining world renown for his humanization of historical figures. Analytical in approach, Ludwig consistently emphasized the psychological motives guiding the actions of his heroes. His best known biographies are those of Goethe (1920-23), Bismarck (1922-23), Napoleon (1924), and Kaiser Wilhelm II (1925), but he also wrote on such widely diverse people as Bolivar, Lincoln, Michelangelo, Beethoven, and Franklin Roosevelt. Although pursuing no original research into the lives of the men of whom he wrote, Ludwig nonetheless created generally accurate and perceptive works in a basically novelistic style.

MENDELE MOCHER S'FORIM
(Solomon Jacob Abramowitsch) (1836-1917)
Born Kopyl, Lithuania; died Odessa, Russia. Writer.
PLAQUE: *Cast bronze, 11⅚₆" x 9". FB 36.*

Mendele Mocher S'forim journeyed throughout Russia as a student and acquired a sound acquaintance with Jewish conditions in that country. Becoming involved before long in the Jewish progressive movement, he published his three-volume *Natural History* (1862-72), a work that awakened great interest in the subject among his fellow Jews. But his major preoccupation was tendentious fiction. His *Little Man* (1864) was a scarcely veiled attack against a government favorite and caused that individual's removal from office. *Fathers and Sons* (1868) was a moving depiction of the struggle between tradition and progress. Written in Hebrew, these works were marked by the wit, pathos, and psychological insight that typified all of his writing. Mendele was one of the first intellectuals to write in Yiddish. He used that language in order to reach the people and became known as the "grandfather of Yiddish literature." He returned to Hebrew in later years and helped to establish modern Hebrew literary style by his use of Biblical, Mishnaic, and Midrashic idioms.

ERICH MENDELSOHN (1887-1953)
Born Allenstein, Germany; died San Francisco, California. Architect.
PLAQUE: *Cast bronze, 5⅜" x 7¼", by B. Simon. FB 1091.*

Among the giants of twentieth-century architecture is Erich Mendelsohn. After study in Munich and Berlin, he settled in the former city, whence gradually his name became known throughout the world. An experimentalist in the use of materials and methods of construction, he seemed to be as much a sculptor as an architect. His Einstein Tower in Potsdam (1921) is a masterpiece of expressionistic architecture. He moved to England in 1933 and four years later built the famous Hotel Blackpool and the Hebrew University Medical Center on Mt. Scopus. In 1941 Mendelsohn came to the United States, where he soon became the foremost synagogue architect in America (St. Louis and Cleveland, 1945). He also built well-known Jewish Centers in Baltimore (1948), Grand Rapids, Michigan (1948), St. Paul (1949), and Dallas (1951). Noted for his inventive use of curves and for the squatness, yet overwhelming power, of his designs, Mendelsohn was one of the most influential architects of the twentieth century.

ANTON RAPHAEL MENGS (1728-1779)
Born Aussig, Bohemia; died Rome, Italy. Painter.
PLAQUE: *Cast bronze, 6¼" x 5⅛", by I. Sors. FB 819.*

Although appointed first painter to the Elector of Saxony, Anton Raphael Mengs spent most of his time in Rome, where after 1754 he was director of the Vatican Academy. Founder of the school of neoclassicism and hailed at the time as the savior of art and the greatest painter in all of Europe, Mengs was one of the most influential artists of the eighteenth century. He was twice commissioned by Charles III of Spain to do paintings in Madrid; his ceiling of the banquet hall in that city is one of his best works. Other outstanding examples of his art are *Perseus and Andromeda* and altarpieces at All Souls' and Magdalen Colleges at the University of Oxford. Mengs also wrote extensive, pedantic works on art theory that were regarded as law for half a century after his death.

FERENC MOLNAR (1878-1952)

Born Budapest, Hungary; died New York City. Dramatist and novelist.
PLAQUE: *Cast bronze, 4⅜″ x 4″, by I. Sors. FB 697.*

Ferenc Molnar (né Neumann) studied at the Universities of Budapest and Geneva. He later wrote for newspapers and periodicals in his native city and in 1902 achieved his first success as a playwright. Five years later he gained international fame with the production of *The Devil.* Triumph followed triumph as he wrote *Liliom* (1909), *The Guardsman* (1910), *Heavenly and Earthly Love* (1919), and *The Swan* (1919). Molnar was a man of very great, though gentle wit, at once sophisticated and sentimental, and his plays were noted for their subtle combination of the banal and the supernatural. He was also the author of several novels, the best known being *The Paul Street Boys* (1907). During World War I Molnar enhanced his already great reputation by his astute reports from the Russian front, where he served as a correspondent. In 1940 he fled Europe and settled in New York City.

MICHAEL von MUNKACSY (1844-1900)

Born Munkács, Hungary; died Bonn, Germany. Painter.
PLAQUE: *Cast bronze, 5⁹⁄₁₆″ x 4⁷⁄₁₆″, by I. Sors. FB 700.*

Michael von Munkacsy (né Tieb) was an apprentice carpenter when in 1858 he ran away with a well-known traveling painter who accepted him as his student. After twelve years of wandering Munkacsy achieved an enormous success in the Paris Salon of 1870 with his *Last Day of a Condemned Prisoner.* Two years later he settled in the French capital. His extraordinary powers of characterization were seen to great advantage in his *Milton Dictating* Paradise Lost *to His Daughters* (1878), *Christ Before Pilate* (1881), *Golgotha* (1883), and *The Death of Mozart* (1884). Munkacsy was one of the very few great non-Impressionist artists of the latter half of the nineteenth century. His works may be found today in major museums throughout the world.

ISAAC LOEB PERETZ (1851-1915)

Born Zamosc, Poland; died Warsaw, Poland. Writer.
PLAQUE: *Cast bronze, 7¼″ x 4¾″, by A. Eisenberg. FB 705.*

Isaac Loeb Peretz was an outstanding student, excelling in both religious and secular studies. He later was a successful attorney, but after ten years government restrictions forced him to discontinue his career. He moved to Warsaw and from 1887 to 1915 served in various capacities as an employee of the Jewish community there. It was at this time that Peretz began in earnest the work that was to make him famous. Writing first in Hebrew and later in Yiddish, he produced numerous short stories that reflected the unconquerable spirit of his people and his own deep love for and understanding of them. He fought valiantly against the existing social order and demanded that his fellow Jews rise from the ghetto and become a part of the larger world around them. Peretz claimed that temporal needs and pleasures are as important as the spiritual and wrote a number of tendentious articles on secular subjects for *Die Yiddishe Bibliothek,* a journal of which he was editor for a number of years.

CAMILLE PISSARRO (1830-1903)

Born St. Thomas, West Indies; died Paris, France. Painter.
PLAQUE: *Cast bronze, 4⁵⁄₁₆″ x 3½″, by I. Sors. FB 754.*

Camille Pissarro completed his studies in Paris and returned to
St. Thomas to enter the family business. Soon, however, his artistic
ambitions called him back to France, where he entered the École des
Beaux Arts. At first he was little more than an imitator of Corot, but
upon his removal to Louvenciennes he began the work that eventually
made him one of the leaders of the Impressionist school of painting.
He fled to London during the Franco-Prussian War but returned to
Paris immediately thereafter and exhibited in the first Impressionist
show (1874). In his many brilliant works Pissarro recorded the atmosphere and color of Rouen and Paris and the day-to-day life of the
French peasant. His interest, however, was not in human figures but
in landscapes, and his numerous colorful depictions of sunlight and its
various effects upon nature are among the finest ever executed.

ARTHUR SCHNITZLER (1862-1931)

Born and died Vienna, Austria. Playwright and novelist.
PLAQUE: *Cast bronze, 5⅜″ x 3¹³⁄₁₆″, by I. Sors. FB 790.*

Arthur Schnitzler, a practicing physician, turned to literature and
achieved a spectacular success with his *Anatol* cycle in 1893. With
humor and delicacy he allowed his characters to create themselves
out of their own unconscious. Even the young Freud was astounded
at the way in which Schnitzler so artistically presented his (Freud's)
as yet unaccepted scientific theories. Schnitzler had a gift of characterization second to none, capturing the spirit of Vienna and her
people in literature as Johann Strauss had done in music. His accurate portraits were at times shattering, but they were never vulgar
or heavy-handed. He observed and wrote with extraordinary self-
possession and never lapsed into overt criticism; his characters spoke
for themselves. Thus even in his treatment of antisemitism he would
hazard no answer, leaving it to the reader (or viewer) to discover
his own solutions. Among his best known works are *Liebelei* (1895),
Professor Bernhardi (1912), and *The Road to the Open* (1908), a
novel.

SHOLOM ALEICHEM (Solomon Rabinowitz) (1859-1916)

Born Pereyaslav, Russia; died Copenhagen, Denmark. Writer.
PLAQUE: *Cast bronze, silver-plated, diam. 2″, by A. Eisenberg. FB 33.*

Sholom Aleichem is best known for his tales of life among the op-
pressed and poverty-stricken Russian Jews of the late nineteenth
century. Like their creator, his characters viewed their little world
philosophically and with laughter. Writing first in Russian and Hebrew, Sholom Aleichem turned to Yiddish in 1883. In 1905 he left
Russia for Switzerland and spent the next nine years lecturing
throughout Europe and the United States. At the beginning of
World War I he moved to America. Known as the "Jewish Mark
Twain," Sholom Aleichem was the first Yiddish author to write stories
especially for children. Stage adaptations of his works formed the
foundation of New York's Yiddish Art Theatre. *Verk* (fourteen volumes, 1908-14) is a collection of his writings, many of which have
since been translated into English.

GERTRUDE STEIN (1874-1946)

Born Allegheny, Pennsylvania; died Paris, France. Writer and art patron.
PLAQUE: *Cast bronze, diam. 6⁵⁄₁₆″, by E. Quattrocchi. FB 1090.*

After attending Radcliffe College (1893-97) and the Johns Hopkins University medical school (1897-1902), Gertrude Stein settled in Paris. Only once did she return to her native country—to give a lecture tour in 1934. Miss Stein was interested far more in the sounds of words than in their meaning and was noted for her weird, repetitious, and daring works. She was one of the most often mocked and parodied authors of the twentieth century, but from her world-famous Paris salon she taught her theories of "literary cubism" to a host of promising young American writers. She had an incalculable influence on such men of the "lost generation" (her own designation for those whose youth was disrupted by World War I) as Sherwood Anderson, Ernest Hemingway, and Thornton Wilder. Her best known works are *Three Lives* (1908), *The Autobiography of Alice B. Toklas* (1933), *Four Saints in Three Acts* (an opera, 1934), and *Wars I Have Seen* (1945). Miss Stein was an intimate friend and early proponent of many great artists, two of whom she wrote about in *Matisse, Picasso, and Gertrude Stein* (1932).

HERMANN STRUCK (1876-1944)

Born Berlin, Germany; died Haifa, Palestine. Etcher and painter.
PLAQUE: *Cast bronze, 5″ x 3⅞″, by I. Sors. FB 533.*

Hermann Struck learned his art by practicing it. During most of his life he traveled throughout Europe—drawing, etching, and painting landscapes. In this way he made of himself one of the foremost etchers of the twentieth century and became perhaps more learned in the technical aspects of this highly developed art form than any other individual. Struck was constantly and deeply moved by the spirit of his people, and some of his finest work is devoted to the depiction of the lives and mores of his fellow Jews. In 1923 he finally settled in Haifa, where, more than anyone else, he aided in the development of the aesthetic tastes of the young men and women who entered the country during the next twenty years. In his later years Struck devoted himself almost entirely to painting, but he never gained the mastery of this art that he had of the difficult art of etching.

JAKOB WASSERMANN (1873-1934)

Born Fürth, Germany; died Alt-Aussee, Austria. Novelist.
PLAQUE: *Cast bronze, 6⁷⁄₁₆″ x 4¹³⁄₁₆″, by I. Sors. FB 603.*

Jakob Wassermann turned to writing after failing in business. He achieved some success with his first novel, *The Jews of Zirndorf* (1896), but it was not until the publication of *The Goose Man* (1915) and *The World's Illusion* (1919) that he gained world fame. In the latter work Wassermann concentrated on the problems that most disturbed him: the lack of justice in the world and the apparently human source of evil. He was a gifted and versatile storyteller who sought, as a moralist, to explore the very bases of human nature. Wassermann fought throughout his life against bigotry. Yet ironically he spent the last year of his life as an exile in Austria—forced to leave his own homeland by the Nazis. Two of his well-known later works are *Gold* (1924) and *The Triumph of Youth* (1926).

MAX WEBER (1881-1961)

Born Bialystok, Russia; died Great Neck, New York. Painter.
PLAQUE: *Cast bronze, 5⅞" x 4⅛", by I. Sors. FB 876.*

Max Weber was graduated from the Normal Art School of Pratt Institute (1900) and attended the Julien Academy in Paris (1905-06). He was a pupil of Laurens and Matisse, and studied further in Spain, Italy, and Holland. While in France, Weber became interested in cubism and primitive art, and on his return to the United States he fought to gain acceptance for modern art. His own early work was greeted with hostility by the critics, but after years of poverty and nonrecognition Weber's work was finally acknowledged. Today he is represented in the collections of the Metropolitan Museum of Art, the Museum of Modern Art, and the Whitney Museum of American Art in New York, as well as in museums and private collections throughout the world. Weber was awarded the Potter Palmer gold medal of the Chicago Art Institute (1928), the bronze medal of the Corcoran Gallery of Art (1942), and the Pennsylvania Academy of Fine Arts' Temple gold medal (1942).

FRANZ WERFEL (1890-1945)

Born Prague, Bohemia; died Hollywood, California. Novelist and playwright.
PLAQUE: *Cast bronze, 6⅜" x 5", by I. Sors. FB 588.*

Franz Werfel, leader of the young literary iconoclasts in Germany after World War I, was educated at the Universities of Prague and Leipzig. He was one of the most distinguished modern German poets (*We Are* [1913] and *Another* [1915]) but achieved his greatest fame as a dramatist and novelist. His *Goat Song* (1922) and *Juarez and Maximilian* (1924) were two of the most successful plays of the decade, and his novels, *The Forty Days of Musa Dagh* (1934), *Embezzled Heaven* (1940), and *The Song of Bernadette* (1942), were known and loved throughout the world. Noted for their beauty of thought and expression, his works proposed the necessity of religion as a means to self-fulfillment. Werfel fled Vienna in 1938 and lived in Paris and Lourdes. When the Nazis conquered France in 1940 he escaped to the United States, where he lived until his death.

ISRAEL ZANGWILL (1864-1926)

Born London, England; died Sussex, England. Writer.
PLAQUE: *Cast bronze, 5¼" x 4", by Kormis. FB 410.*

Israel Zangwill was educated at the Jews' Free School (where he taught after the age of fourteen) and at the University of London. He first attracted attention as the author of the beautiful *Children of the Ghetto* (1892). Portraying life in the ghetto with infinite humor, pathos, and poetry, Zangwill contended that the vast majority of problems faced by world Jewry were based in its stubborn refusal to discard or update many outmoded traditions. He was outspoken in his advocacy of the removal of all racial and national barriers but was nonetheless an ardent Zionist. He considered Palestine to be unsuitable for mass settlement, however, and served as president of the Jewish Territorial Organization for the Settlement of Jews Within the British Empire. Zangwill was champion of many unpopular causes (women's suffrage, for example), but was beloved as the author of *Ghetto Tragedies* (1893), *Dreamers of the Ghetto* (1898), and the very popular *Merely Mary Ann* (1903).

[121]

ARNOLD ZWEIG (1887-   )

Born Glogau, Germany. Novelist.
PLAQUE: *Cast bronze, 6⅛" x 4¹¹⁄₁₆", by I. Sors. FB 584.*

Arnold Zweig was educated at seven European universities (including Breslau, Berlin, and Göttingen). He wrote for many years but did not gain fame until 1927, when his *Case of Sergeant Grischa* brought him the critical and popular acclaim of the entire world. It was the story of a Russian prisoner of war and entailed a relentless depiction of Prussian bureaucracy and of the cruel impact of war on society. Zweig was emotionally involved with the characters of this great work and later wrote three highly successful sequels: *Young Woman of 1914* (1931), *Education Before Verdun* (1935), and *The Crowning of a King* (1937). He was exiled from Germany in 1933 and settled in Palestine, but he returned to East Germany after World War II. Long a critic of the injustices perpetrated by capitalist societies, Zweig was recipient of the Lenin Award in 1958.

STEFAN ZWEIG (1881-1942)

Born Vienna, Austria; died Petropolis, Brazil. Biographer and novelist.
PLAQUE: *Cast bronze, diam. 3¹⁵⁄₁₆", by I. Sors. FB 760.*

Stefan Zweig first came onto the literary scene in 1913 with his biography of Paul Verlaine. He was a man of great sensitivity, and the horrors of World War I led him to write his symbolic dramatic poem *Jeremiah* (1917) with a bitterness that was to remain with him for the rest of his life. Although he was not a disciple of Emil Ludwig, Zweig was nonetheless distinctly a member of the new school of biography. He made use of his acute judgmental powers and poetic imagination and strove to re-create the psychological forces that lay behind the actions of his subjects. Among his best works are *Three Masters (Balzac, Dickens, and Dostoievsky)* (1920), *Marie Antoinette* (1932), and *The Story of Magellan* (1938). Zweig was not only extremely popular as a biographer, but also met with considerable success as a novelist. He left Austria in 1938 and came to the United States. In 1941 Zweig went to Brazil, where his thirty years' disillusionment and ten years of despair at Nazi success led to his suicide in 1942.

Music
&
Theater

GREAT JEWISH PORTRAITS IN METAL

DAVID BELASCO (1854-1931)

Born San Francisco, California; died New York City. Playwright, actor, and producer.
PLAQUE: *Cast bronze, 7" x 4¾", by A. Eisenberg. FB 779.*

David Belasco began his theatrical career as a bareback rider, thence graduating to the roles of barker, actor, stage manager, and playwright. In 1882 he went to New York, where he revolutionized stage technique by using Edison's new electric light. Soon he formed an association with Daniel Frohman, gained ownership of numerous theatres, and by 1926 had over three hundred players under contract. Belasco was unquestionably the greatest producer of his day. Among his successes were the works of his own pen: *Du Barry* (1901), *The Girl of the Golden West* (1905), and *The Return of Peter Grimes* (1911). *The Girl of the Golden West* and *Madame Butterfly* (1900), which he adapted from a popular novel of the time, were transformed into successful operas by Giacomo Puccini. Without equal as a creator of stars and stage effects, Belasco was noted for productions combining scenic realism, impeccable detail, and inventive lighting.

IRVING BERLIN (1888-   )

Born Mologa, Russia. Composer.
PLAQUE: *Cast bronze, 4" x 2¾", by I. Sors. FB 627.*

The son of a cantor, Irving Berlin was brought to the United States in 1893. He was a singing waiter on New York's Lower East Side when in 1911 the publication of "Alexander's Ragtime Band" brought him overnight fame. In 1920 Berlin went into partnership with Sam Harris, built the Music Box Theatre, and wrote the scores for the four *Music Box Revues*. Among his major Broadway successes are *As Thousands Cheer* (1933), *Louisiana Purchase* (1940), *Annie Get Your Gun* (1946), and *Call Me Madam* (1950). One of the most prolific and successful composers of modern popular music, Berlin is the recipient of a Congressional gold medal for his song, "God Bless America." He was also awarded the Medal of Merit for *This Is the Army* (1942), the proceeds of which were donated to the United States Government for defense work.

SARAH BERNHARDT (1844-1923)

Born and died Paris, France. Actress.
MEDAL: *Struck silver, 1¹⁵⁄₁₆" x 1½", by P. Fritz. FB 61.*

Sarah Bernhardt made her debut at the Comédie Française in 1862, after study at the Conservatoire Français. She was a brilliant exponent of classical and romantic roles, and it was but a very short time before she had become the foremost actress in France. Among her greatest successes were her characterizations in Racine's *Phèdre*, Rostand's *L'Aiglon*, Dumas' *La Dame aux Camélias*, and Shakespeare's *Hamlet*. Her portrayal of the Prince of Denmark was one of the best known of modern times. The "divine Sarah" (as she was called by Victor Hugo) continued her magnificent career until the end of her life, performing on a couch after the amputation of a leg in 1914. Coupled with renown for voice and gesture, Miss Bernhardt's name became a synonym for thespian perfection. She served as the model for the character of Berma in Marcel Proust's *Remembrance of Things Past*.

ERNEST BLOCH (1880-1959)

Born Geneva, Switzerland; died Portland, Oregon. Composer.
PLAQUE: *Cast bronze, 6⁵⁄₁₆″ x 5¹⁄₁₆″, by I. Sors. FB 591.*

Ernest Bloch studied harmonics, violin, and composition in various
musical centers of Europe and conducted in Lausanne and Neuchâtel.
His opera *Macbeth* was enthusiastically received at its Paris premiere
in 1909, as was his First Symphony in 1915. It was at this time that
Bloch's music first became Hebraic in style and character. He once
said: "It is the Jewish soul that interests me, the complex, glowing,
agitated soul that I feel vibrating throughout the Bible." It was this
interest that led to such works as *Two Psalms* (114 and 137), *Trois
Poèmes Juifs*, the "Schelomo" Rhapsody for Cello and Orchestra, and
the "Israel" Symphony. The Piano Quartet, considered by many to
be his masterpiece, is a deeply religious work reflecting Hassidic mysticism. In 1916 Bloch came to the United States, where he held the
directorships of the Cleveland Institute of Music (1920-25) and of
the San Francisco Conservatory (1925-30).

LEOPOLD DAMROSCH (1832-1885)

Born Posen, Germany; died New York City. Conductor and composer.
PLAQUE: *Cast bronze, 5¼″ x 3¾″, by I. Sors. FB 477.*

As a child, Leopold Damrosch secretly studied the violin against his parents' wishes. To please them he attended the University of Berlin and practiced medicine for a short period. In 1856 he appeared as violinist at Magdeburg and soon became solo violinist in Franz Liszt's famous ducal orchestra at Weimar. Director of the Stadttheater in Posen and conductor of the Breslau Philharmonic, he came to the United States in 1871 and within three years had organized the famous Oratorio Society of New York. In 1878 he founded the Symphony Society of New York and six years later introduced German opera at the Metropolitan Opera House. One of the most illustrious figures in American musical circles of the late nineteenth century, Damrosch was also composer of seven cantatas, a symphony, and an opera *(Sulamith)*. His son, Walter (1862-1950), gained equal prominence as conductor of the New York Symphony Orchestra (1885-1926).

MISCHA ELMAN (1891-   )

Born Stalnoje, Russia. Violinist.
PLAQUE: *Cast bronze, diam. 5¾″, by A. Eisenberg. FB 657.*

Mischa Elman began his study of the violin at the age of four. His first teacher was his father, but later Leopold Auer arranged for him to study at the St. Petersburg Conservatory free of charge. At his initial concert (Berlin, 1904) he was acclaimed as the greatest of all child prodigies. This reputation followed him and was reinforced throughout his subsequent European tour. One of the most talented and technically impeccable violinists of the twentieth century, Elman has been in outstanding demand in the United States since his American debut in 1908. Appearing regularly in concert and recital, Elman has given perhaps more benefit performances than any other violinist—in one year alone he gave twenty-six concerts to aid German and Austrian refugees of all faiths. His popularity has been further enhanced by the many recordings he has made.

OSSIP GABRILOWITSCH (1878-1936)

Born St. Petersburg, Russia; died Detroit, Michigan. Pianist and conductor.
PLAQUE: *Cast bronze, diam. 5″, by Simpson. FB 54.*

Ossip Gabrilowitsch studied music at the Imperial Conservatory under Anton Rubinstein and in 1894 won the coveted Rubinstein prize. He went to Vienna, where he continued his studies, and in 1896 made a highly successful European concert tour. Fourteen years later he settled in Munich and turned to conducting, soon increasing the fame that he had achieved throughout the world by his mastery of the piano. He emigrated to the United States in 1914 with his wife Clara, the daughter of Mark Twain. Four years later he became conductor of the Detroit Symphony. As a conductor he was distinguished for the same qualities that had made him so successful as a pianist: subtlety, sensitivity, reflectiveness, and variety of mood and phrasing. Under his leadership for eighteen years, the Detroit Symphony became one of the foremost orchestras in the United States.

GEORGE GERSHWIN (1898-1937)

Born Brooklyn, New York; died Beverly Hills, California. Composer.
PLAQUE: *Cast bronze, 6" x 5", by A. Eisenberg. FB 662.*

Educated in the New York public school system, George Gershwin learned music by listening and, to a lesser extent, by studies in piano, harmony, and musical theory. This happy combination of theory and classical music and music as heard on the streets of New York in the early twentieth century produced the "sophisticated jazz" for which Gershwin became famous. After writing the popular *George White's Scandals* (1920-24), he gained acceptance in serious musical circles throughout the world with *Rhapsody in Blue* (1924), the composition that freed jazz from the confines of Tin Pan Alley. Overnight Gershwin had destroyed the barrier between classical and popular music. Later orchestral pieces included *Concerto in F* (1925) for piano and orchestra, *An American in Paris* (1928), and the *Cuban Overture* (1932). Among his best known musical comedies are *Lady Be Good* (1924), *Oh Kay* (1926), *Girl Crazy* (1930), and *Of Thee I Sing* (1931). His *Porgy and Bess* (1935) has become a classic.

JACQUES FRANÇOIS FROMENTHAL ÉLIE HALÉVY (1799-1862)

Born Paris, France; died Nice, France. Composer.
PLAQUE: *Cast bronze, diam. 4⁹⁄₁₆", by S. Hovell. FB 488.*

Jacques Halévy entered the Paris Conservatory when he was only ten years old and later studied for five years under the Italian master, Cherubini. Halévy's cantata *Herminie* won the Grand Prix de Rome. In 1820 his *De Profundis*, with Hebrew text, was performed in a Paris synagogue. From 1827 to 1840 Halévy taught harmony, counterpoint, and advanced composition at the Paris Conservatory, where he numbered among his students Saint-Saëns, Gounod, and Bizet (his son-in-law). Of his many operas, his best known is *La Juive* (1835), which he wrote at the peak of his creative powers. Still played throughout the world, it is perhaps his most representative work, filled with appealing lyricism and flawless instrumentation and harmony. Halévy was a member of the French Academy and after 1840 was professor of composition at the Conservatory.

HARRY HOUDINI (1874-1926)

Born Appleton, Wisconsin; died Detroit, Michigan. Magician and author.
PLAQUE: *Cast bronze, 4½" x 3³⁄₁₆", by I. Sors. FB 500.*

Son of a rabbi and scholar, Harry Houdini (né Ehrich Weiss) developed his interest in magic and feats of dexterity through various odd jobs that he held in his youth. He performed in a number of circuses and traveling shows and was soon one of the most sought-after entertainers of his day. A master showman who made use of his expert knowledge of mechanics to become the world's foremost escape artist, Houdini achieved international fame in 1900 by escaping from Scotland Yard. His incomparable collection of books, playbills, and prints on magic and spiritualism and his fine drama library and collection of manuscripts were bequeathed to the Library of Congress. A highly popular, if specialized, author, he wrote *Miracle Mongers and Their Methods* (1920) and *A Magician Among the Spirits* (1924).

BRONISLAW HUBERMANN (1882-1947)

Born Czestochowa, Poland; died Nant-sur-Corsier, Switzerland. Violinist.
PLAQUE: *Cast bronze, 5³⁄₁₆″ x 5½″, by I. Sors. FB 637.*

Bronislaw Hubermann began his study of the violin at the age of six and made his first public appearance a year later. Continuing his study under many famous European violinists and teachers, in 1893 Hubermann toured Europe and was received with acclaim throughout the continent. He made his first tour of the United States in 1898-99 and remained to play with great success for many years. In 1903 he was invited to play in Genoa on Paganini's Guarnerius violin, an honor accorded to only one violinist before him. Twenty years later Hubermann forcefully denounced the Hitler regime, refusing to play in a country ruled by a tyrant. Visiting Palestine in 1935, he began efforts to form a Palestine Symphony Orchestra. His work met with success and the orchestra made its debut, led by Arturo Toscanini, on December 26, 1936. It since has taken its place as one of the foremost symphony orchestras in the world.

JOSEF JOACHIM (1831-1907)

Born Kittsee, Hungary; died Berlin, Germany. Violinist and composer.
MEDAL: *Cast bronze, diam. 2⁵⁄₁₆″, by I. Sors. FBG 132.*

Josef Joachim studied in Budapest, made his debut there at the age of eight, and four years later entered the conservatory at Leipzig. After numerous successes throughout Europe, he was asked by Franz Liszt to serve as *konzertmeister* at Weimar (1850) and three years later was named *konzertmeister* to the king at Hanover. In 1869 he was appointed head of the newly established Hochschule für Musik in Berlin. The following year he organized the Joachim String Quartet, the famed ensemble that was largely responsible for the enormous popularity of the Beethoven string quartets. Possessed of unsurpassed insight into the music he played, Joachim was the acknowledged master among nineteenth-century violinists. His performances were noted for their dignity and became the standard by which all other violinists were judged. Although he is best known as a performer, his numerous compositions for the violin are still found in the standard repertoire.

GUSTAV MAHLER (1860-1911)

Born Kalisch, Bohemia; died Vienna, Austria. Composer and conductor.
MEDAL: *Cast bronze, diam. 4¹⁵⁄₁₆″, by B. Elkan. FB 57.*

Gustav Mahler had conducted in Leipzig, Prague, Budapest, and Hamburg when he gained the attention of Johannes Brahms and, upon the recommendation of the great master, was appointed (1897) to the coveted post of director of the Vienna Imperial Opera. Ten years later he came to the United States, where he conducted with both the New York Philharmonic and the Metropolitan Opera. His outstanding characteristics as a conductor were warmth and immense power, qualities that not only infused his interpretations but also his own compositions. Greatly influenced by Richard Wagner and the romantic movement, he wrote nine symphonies (for an orchestra nearly doubled in size) and several song cycles with orchestra. His music has been called "gigantic," "audacious," and "grotesque." But there is no question about Mahler's great originality, and his works are now a part of the repertoire of orchestras throughout the world.

FELIX MENDELSSOHN-BARTHOLDY (1809-1847)

Born Hamburg, Germany; died Leipzig, Germany. Composer.
MEDAL: *Cast bronze, diam. 1½", by Weckwerth. FB 59.*

Felix Mendelssohn, the grandson of Moses Mendelssohn, gained renown as a pianist and composer while still a child. His reputation
was unquestioned after the first performance of his overture to *A
Midsummer Night's Dream* (1826), later expanded (1843) to include
incidental music for Shakespeare's great comedy. Having served
as musical director in Düsseldorf and Leipzig, Mendelssohn
was called by the king of Prussia to serve as *kapellmeister* in Berlin.
Dissatisfied there, however, he returned to Leipzig, where in 1843
he founded the world-famous conservatory. Among his many im-
mortal works are the "Reformation" (1830-32), "Scottish" (1830-42),
and "Italian" (1833) Symphonies, the *Songs Without Words* (1832-
45), and his brilliant oratorios, *St. Paul* (1836) and *Elijah* (1846).
Mendelssohn is also known as the rediscoverer of Bach, whose *St.
Matthew Passion* he conducted in 1829 in the first known performance
of a Bach choral work since 1750 and at a time when not one of the
great master's works was in print.

[129]

DANIEL MENDOZA (1763-1836)

Born and died London, England. Pugilist.
MEDAL: *Cast copper, diam. 1⅛", artist unknown. FB 238.*

The owner of a London public house, The Admiral Nelson, Daniel Mendoza was the most noted pugilist of his day—not because of his strength but because of his great skill. With Mendoza's entrance onto the scene, boxing ceased to be a mere contest of brute force and began to develop into a science. He originated the art of footwork and, utilizing a primitive psychological approach toward his opponents, was the first fighter to emphasize the importance of defense and defense *tactics* rather than, or as well as, mere brutal offense. As champion of England from 1792 to 1795, Mendoza was known throughout England and Ireland as the "Star of Israel." He made numerous exhibition tours and fought his last fight at the age of fifty-seven.

GIACOMO MEYERBEER (1791-1864)

Born Berlin, Germany; died Paris, France. Composer.
MEDAL: *Cast bronze, diam. 1¹⁵⁄₁₆", by C. Rodnitzky. FB 51.*

Giacomo Meyerbeer (Jakob Meyer Beer) first gained fame when he appeared as a pianist at the age of seven. After studying with Bernard Weber (director of the Berlin Opera), he went to Darmstadt, where in 1812 he was appointed court composer. He met with a number of operatic failures both there and in Vienna, and later moved to Italy, where within a very brief time he produced seven highly popular operas. At first a mere imitator of Rossini, it was not until his removal to Paris in 1826 that he truly came into his own as a composer. *Robert le Diable* (1831) was the first romantic grand opera and was an immediate sensation, due particularly to its exquisite ballet music. As *kapellmeister* to the king of Prussia (1842-49) he produced very little of his own but strove with a measure of success for the popular acceptance of the operas of Weber and Wagner. Among Meyerbeer's best known works are *Les Huguenots* (1836), *Le Prophète* (1849), *Dinorah* (1859), and *L'Africaine* (1864).

JACQUES OFFENBACH (1819-1880)

Born Cologne, Germany; died Paris, France. Composer.
PLAQUE: *Cast bronze, diam. 5⅛", by Hovell. FB 702.*

The son of a cantor, Jacques Offenbach studied under Cherubini at the Paris Conservatory. At the age of fifteen he was cellist with the Opéra-Comique and soon became a ubiquitous concert performer. During this period he studied composition with Jacques Halévy. From 1844 to 1855 he played in Parisian salons and wrote a number of undistinguished (and unsuccessful) operettas. In 1855, however, he hired a small theatre in which to produce his musical farce *Les Deux Aveugles* and became an overnight sensation. In the course of his lengthy career Offenbach composed more than one hundred operettas, among them *La Périchole* and *Orphée aux enfers*, the overture to the latter containing the music known today as the cancan. Offenbach's one grand opera, *Les Contes d'Hoffmann*, is considered his finest work and remains one of the most popular of all French operas.

RACHEL (Élisa-Rachel Félix) (1821-1858)

Born Mumpf, Switzerland; died Cannet, France. Actress.
MEDAL: *Struck bronze, diam. 2¹⁄₁₆″, by F. Pinguet. FB 62.*

Rachel was the daughter of a peddler and, until her family moved to Paris in 1830, helped to support her parents by singing and dancing in the streets and cafés. In Paris, however, she was made the protégée of a wealthy Frenchman and in 1833 entered the conservatory. Five years later she made her debut in Corneille's *Horace.* Her greatness was immediately recognized, and all Europe acclaimed her when in 1841 she toured England and the continent. Her characterization of Racine's *Phèdre,* which she played for two years and whose success saved the Comédie Française from bankruptcy, was one of the most famous portrayals of the nineteenth century. Rachel was particularly noted for the restraint of her acting and the majesty and dignity with which she impersonated evil characters.

MAX REINHARDT (1873-1943)

Born Baden, Austria; died New York City. Actor, director, and producer.
PLAQUE: *Cast bronze, 4⅝″ x 3⅜″, by I. Sors. FB 714.*

Max Reinhardt met with stunning success as a young actor, and in 1905 he formed his own theatre. He was soon known throughout the world for his highly original, impressionistic productions of the classics (Molière, Goethe, Schiller) and of the more modern masters (Strindberg, Ibsen, Shaw). Particularly notable were his modern-dress version of *Hamlet* and the spectacular production of *A Midsummer Night's Dream,* with which he introduced the revolving stage. Two of Reinhardt's most unusual triumphs were the silent pageant *The Miracle* (1911) and *Everyman* (1920), a medieval morality play which was an annual feature at the Salzburg Festival until it was prohibited by the Nazis. After 1934 his main interest was the Max Reinhardt Workshop in Hollywood, which he directed. Recipient of many honorary degrees, Reinhardt was one of the most artistically inventive producers and directors of the twentieth century.

ANTON GRIGORIEVICH RUBINSTEIN (1829-1894)

Born Vykhovatinets, Russia; died Peterhof, Russia. Pianist and composer.
PLAQUE: *Cast bronze, 2″ x 1½″, by M. W. St. FB 55.*

Trained primarily by his mother, Anton Rubinstein made his Moscow debut as a pianist in 1839. Thus he began a career that would bring him renown as the equal (if not the superior) of the master himself, Franz Liszt. Returning to St. Petersburg after study in Berlin (1844-48) and Vienna (1848-54), Rubinstein was appointed court pianist in 1858. Four years later he founded the world-famous St. Petersburg Conservatory, serving twice as its director (1862-67; 1887-90) and, in the interval, touring Europe and America to unceasing acclaim and adulation. His own compositions, although they retained the brilliance and technical perfection of his piano playing, never won wide acceptance; however, his reputation as one of the greatest of nineteenth-century masters remains secure. In 1889, following his return to the directorship of the Conservatory at St. Petersburg, he published his well-known *Autobiography*.

RUDOLPH SCHILDKRAUT (1862-1930)

Born Wallachia, Romania; died Hollywood, California. Actor.
PLAQUE: *Cast bronze, diam. 6⅛", by A. Eisenberg. FB 427.*

Rudolph Schildkraut, one of the most gifted and versatile actors of his generation, first gained fame as a character actor in Germany and Austria. In 1905 he became a leading member of Max Reinhardt's company and was soon known and admired throughout the world. Schildkraut was particularly acclaimed as a Shakespearean actor: his characterizations of Shylock and King Lear were among the finest of the twentieth century. In 1911 he came to the United States and that same year founded a Yiddish art theatre in Brooklyn, where for the next eleven seasons he achieved success in both the classical and modern repertoires. Schildkraut was the father of the well-known actor Joseph Schildkraut, who in 1937 won a motion picture Academy Award for his portrayal of Alfred Dreyfus in *The Life of Émile Zola*.

ARNOLD SCHÖNBERG (1874-1951)

Born Vienna, Austria; died Brentwood, California. Composer.
PLAQUE: *Cast bronze, 4⅞" x 3¹³⁄₁₆", by I. Sors. FB 100.*

Arnold Schönberg began composing chamber music at an early age. Virtually self-taught, he was a true pioneer whose striving for compactness and simplicity led him to write terse, dramatic pieces for small ensembles. After 1915 his atonal, expressionistic works were generally written in the twelve-tone harmonic system, which he invented and which is a distinguishing feature of much modern music. Schönberg taught in Vienna, Amsterdam, and Berlin. In 1933 he came to the United States and served as professor of music at the University of California in Los Angeles from 1936 to 1944. Among his finest works are the *Gurrelieder* (*Songs of the Dove*, a ballad cycle for chorus and orchestra, 1912-13), *Pierrot Lunaire* (1923), and several pieces for string ensembles and chamber orchestras. Schönberg was also author of the important *Theory of Harmony* (1911).

BRUNO WALTER (1876-1962)

Born Berlin, Germany; died Beverly Hills, California. Conductor.
PLAQUE: *Cast bronze, 5½" x 4¹¹⁄₁₆", by I. Sors. FB 590.*

Bruno Walter (né Schlesinger) studied in Berlin and served for short periods as conductor in Cologne, Hamburg, Breslau, Pressburg, and Riga. He was conductor of the Imperial Opera in Vienna (1901-12) and of the Munich Royal Opera (1913-22) and later served both in Leipzig (1929-33) and with the Vienna State Opera (1935-38). In 1938 Walter went to France and the following year came to the United States, where from 1947 to 1950 he was director of the New York Philharmonic. One of the foremost (and most beloved) musicians of the twentieth century, Walter was known alike for his interpretations of opera and orchestral music. He never claimed to be a musicologist and sought no unusual effects in his music. Unlike many of his noted contemporaries he played only what he considered beautiful. Walter, a close friend of Gustav Mahler, was in large part responsible for the popular acceptance that Mahler has been accorded in recent years.

EFREM ZIMBALIST (1889-   )

Born Rostow-on-Don, Russia. Violinist, composer, and educator.
PLAQUE: *Cast bronze, 6" x 4⅝", by I. Sors. FB 749.*

Efrem Zimbalist studied the violin under Leopold Auer at the St. Petersburg Conservatory and made his debut in Berlin at the age of eighteen. His playing was noted for its impeccable taste and stylistic perfection. Zimbalist first appeared in America in 1911, after having met with considerable success in Europe. Three years later he married the great Metropolitan Opera soprano Alma Gluck (1884-1938), and for many years thereafter they appeared on the concert stage in the brilliant joint recitals of which neither the critics nor the public ever tired. In 1928 Zimbalist joined the world-famous Curtis Institute of Music in Philadelphia and thirteen years later became its director, a position that he holds to this day. He is the composer of *American Rhapsody*, a string quartet, a violin sonata, and numerous songs.

Historical
Medals

GREAT JEWISH PORTRAITS IN METAL

Medal commemorating the building of the Synagogue for the "Israelitische Religions-Gesellschaft, Schuetzen-Strasse," Frankfurt-am-Main, 1852.

Silver, diam. 1½". FB 194.

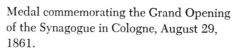

Medal commemorating the Grand Opening of the Synagogue in Cologne, August 29, 1861.

Bronze, diam. 2⅜". FB 197.

Medal commemorating the Inauguration of the new Temple of the Jews in Vercelli, Italy, 1878.

Bronze, diam. 1⅞". FB 199.

Medal commemorating the founding of the B'nai B'rith Lodge in Frankfurt-am-Main, 1902.

Lead, diam. 1⅝". FB 200R.

Medal commemorating the 100th anniversary of Congregation B'nai Jeshurun, New York City, 1925.

Cast bronze, diam. 3¹⁵⁄₁₆". FB 200U.

Medal honoring Albert Cohn, French scholar, who received assurance from Sultan 'Abdal-Magid that the Jews in Palestine would receive equal rights with the Christians. Paris, 1877.

Bronze, diam. 2³⁄₁₆", by G.B.M. and A.M.I. FB 207.

Medal issued by the French Jews in honor of Emperor Napoleon III of France at the time of the Franco-Prussian War, 1870.

Silver, formerly gilded, diam. 2". FB 210.

Medal honoring Gabriel Riesser for his effort in advocating the Emancipation of the Jews, Hamburg, 1836.

Bronze, diam. 2$\frac{5}{16}$". FB 226.

Medal commemorating the 250th anniversary of Jewish settlement in the United States, 1904.

Bronze, diam. 3". FB 227.

Medal of homage by the City of Breslau for Frederick the Great when he entered the city victoriously, 1741.

Copper, diam. 1$\frac{15}{16}$". FB 321.

Medal commemorating the granting of equal rights for Austrian Jews by Emperor Franz Joseph, 1860.

Pewter, diam. 2$\frac{15}{16}$" by P. Seiden. FB 225.

Medal commemorating the Golden Wedding Anniversary of Freiherr Wilhelm Karl and Freifrau Mathilde von Rothschild, November 8, 1899.

Gold, diam. 1$\frac{9}{16}$", unique example in gold. FB 247.

Medal commemorating the 200th anniversary of the Portuguese Synagogue in Amsterdam.

Aluminum, diam. 1$\frac{3}{8}$". FB 213.

Medal commemorating the 100th anniversary of the Philantropin in Frankfurt, one of the first Jewish high schools in Germany, founded in 1804. Frankfurt, 1904.
Bronze, diam. 2⁹⁄₁₆″, FB 204, FBG 36.

Medal commemorating the founding of "The Hebrew National School of Birmingham, England." Foundation stone laid by Sir Moses Montefiore, August 9, 5603 (1843 C. E.).
Bronze, diam. 1¾″. FB 203.

Medal commemorating the marriage of Siegmund Rosenbaum and Dora Hamburger. Frankfurt-am-Main, Mannheim, Grebenstein, 1898. Typical example of a bourgeois marriage medal showing the marriage canopy with two family coats-of-arms over two hands united.
Silver, diam. 1½″. FB 265.

Plaque commemorating the work and merits of Theodor Herzl, January 20, 1904.
Cast bronze, 1⅝″ x ⁹⁄₁₆″, by Boris Schatz.
FB 367.

Medal presented by the Hessian Jews to the Landgraefin Caroline Henrietta, 1790.
Silver, diam. 1³⁄₁₆″. FB 218.

Medal-Amulet (Pilgrim Medal). Jerusalem, c. 1310. The Menorah Tree of Life.

Gold, diam. 2". S 185.

Official insignia worn by Jewish Field Rabbis during World War I (1914-1918); worn by Rabbi Jacob Saenger.

Brass, diam. 2⅞". FB 205.

Medal commemorating the French fighters in the Israeli Sinai Campaign, 1957.

Nickel-silver, diam. 3⅛". FB 1093.

Biblical medal: the two spies sent by Moses to Canaan.

Cast bronze, diam. 1¹⁵⁄₁₆", by Master A.Z., 1914. FB 175.

Biblical medal: Jacob's dream.

Silver, gilded, diam. 1¹⁵⁄₁₆", by Wolf Milicz, 1544. FB 171.

Biblical medal: Adam and Eve.

Silver, diam. 2⅜", by Lucas Richter, 1565. FB 289.

Biblical medal: David and Jonathan.

Silver, diam. 2¼". FB 182.

I N D E X